THE UNIVERSE IN THE LIGHT
OF MODERN PHYSICS

THE UNIVERSE IN THE LIGHT OF MODERN PHYSICS

by

DR. MAX PLANCK

*Professor of Theoretical Physics at the
University of Berlin*

Translated by

W. H. JOHNSTON, B.A.

NEW EDITION
with a new section on Free-Will

LONDON
GEORGE ALLEN & UNWIN LTD
MUSEUM STREET

The present work is a translation of three books, "Das Weltbild der neuen Physik," "Physikalische Gesetzlichkeit im Lichte neuerer Forschung," and "Vom Wesen der Willensfreiheit" (1937), published by Joh. A. Barth in Leipzig. The three works have been run into one, the second here commencing on p. 58, and the third being inserted between p. 85 (second paragraph) and the beginning of section 7.

FIRST PUBLISHED IN ENGLISH (WITHOUT "VOM WESEN DER WILLENSFREIHEIT") 1931

THIS, SECOND, EDITION PUBLISHED 1937

Printed in Great Britain by
UNWIN BROTHERS LIMITED, LONDON AND WOKING

THE UNIVERSE IN THE LIGHT OF MODERN PHYSICS

§ I

PHYSICS is an exact Science and hence depends upon measurement, while all measurement itself requires sense-perception. Consequently all the ideas employed in Physics are derived from the world of sense-perception. It follows from this that the laws of Physics ultimately refer to events in the world of the senses; and in view of this fact many scientists and philosophers tend to the belief that at bottom Physics is concerned exclusively with this particular world. What they have in mind, of course, is the world of man's senses. On this view, for example, what is called an "Object" in ordinary parlance is, when regarded from the standpoint of Physics, simply a combination of different sense-data localized in one place. It is worth pointing out that this view cannot be refuted by logic, since logic itself is unable to lead us beyond the confines of our own senses; it cannot even compel one to admit the independent existence of others outside oneself.

In Physics, however, as in every other science, common sense alone is not supreme; there must also be a place for Reason. Further, the mere absence of logical contradiction does not necessarily imply that everything is reasonable. Now reason tells us that if we turn our back upon a so-called object and cease to attend to it, the object still continues to exist. Reason tells us further that both the individual man and mankind as a whole, together with the entire world which we apprehend through our senses, is no more than a tiny fragment in the vastness of Nature, whose laws are in no way affected by any human brain. On the contrary, they existed long before there was any life on earth, and will continue to exist long after the last physicist has perished.

It is considerations of this kind, and not any logical argument, that compel us to assume the existence of another world of reality behind the world of the senses; a world which has existence independent of man, and which can only be perceived indirectly through the medium of the world of the senses, and by means of certain symbols which our senses allow us to apprehend. It is as though we were compelled to contemplate a certain object in which we are interested through spectacles of whose optical properties we were entirely ignorant.

If the reader experiences difficulty in following this argument, and finds himself unable to accept the idea of a real world which at the same time is expressly asserted to lie beyond our senses, we might point out that there is a vast difference between a physical theory complete in every detail, and the construction of such a theory. In the former case the content of the theory can be analysed exactly, so that it is possible to prove at every point that the notions which we apply to the world of sense are adequate to the formulation of this theory; in the latter case we must develop a theory from a number of individual measurements. The second problem is very much more difficult, while the history of Physics shows that whenever it has been solved, this has been done on the assumption of a real world independent of our senses; and it seems reasonably certain that this will continue to be the case in the future.

But besides the world of sense and the real world, there is also a third world which must be carefully distinguished from these:—this is the world of Physics. It differs from the two others because it is a deliberate hypothesis put forward

by a finite human mind; and as such, it is subject to change and to a kind of evolution. Thus
the function of this world of Physics may be
described in two ways, according as it is related
to the real world, or to the world of the senses.
In the first case the problem is to apprehend the
real world as completely as possible; in the second,
to describe the world of the senses in the simplest
possible terms. There is no need, however, to
assign superior merit to either of these formulations, since each of them, taken by itself alone,
is incomplete and unsatisfactory. On the one
hand, the real world cannot be apprehended
directly at all; while on the other no definite
answer is possible to the question:—Which is the
simplest description of a given number of inter-
dependent sense-perceptions? In the history of
Physics it has happened more than once that,
of two descriptions, one was for a time considered
the more complicated but was later discovered
to be the simpler of the two.

The essential point therefore is that these two
formulations of the problem, when practically
applied, shall be complementary to each other
and not contradictory. The first is an indispensable aid to the groping imagination of the
investigator, supplying him with ideas without

which his work remains unfruitful; the second provides him with a firm foundation of facts. In actual practice individual physicists are influenced in their investigations by their personal preference for metaphysical, or for positivist, ideas. But besides the metaphysicians and the positivists there is a third group of students who investigate the world from the physical point of view. They differ from the first two groups in being interested not so much in the relation between the world of physics on the one hand, and the real world and the world of sense-data on the other, as in the internal consistency and logical structure of the world of physics. These men form the axiomatic school, whose activity is as necessary and useful as is that of the others. At the same time, they are equally exposed to the danger of specialization which, in their case, would lead to a barren formalism taking the place of a fuller understanding of the world of Physics. For as soon as contact with reality has been lost, physical law ceases to be felt as the relation between a number of magnitudes which have been ascertained independently of one another, and becomes a mere definition by which one of these magnitudes is derived from the others. In this method there is a particular attraction, due to the fact that a physical magnitude can be defined far more exactly by means of an equation than by means of measurement. But at the same time, this method amounts to a renunciation of the true meaning of magnitude; while it must also be remembered that confusion and misunderstanding result when the same name is retained in order to denote a changed meaning.

We see, then, how physicists are at work in different directions and from different standpoints in elaborating a systematic view of the world of Physics. Nevertheless the aim of all these endeavours is the same, and consists in establishing a law which connects the events of the world of sense with one another and with those of the real world. Naturally, these different tendencies predominated in turn at different stages of history. Whenever the physical world presented a stable appearance, as in the second half of the last century, the metaphysical view tended to predominate, and it was believed that a complete grasp of the real world was relatively near. Conversely, in times of change and insecurity like the present, positivism tends to occupy the foreground; for in such times a careful student will tend to seek support where he can find real security; and this is to be found precisely in the events of the world of the senses.

Now if we consider the different forms which the view of the physical world has taken in the course of history, and if we look for the peculiarities which characterized these changes, two facts will strike us with special force. First, it is plain that when regarded as a whole, all the changes in the different views of the world of Physics do not constitute a rhythmical swing of the pendulum. On the contrary, we find a clear course of evolution making more or less steady progress in a definite direction; progress which is best described by saying that it adds to the content of the world of sense, rendering our knowledge more profound and giving us a firmer grasp of it. The most striking instance of this is found in the practical application of Physics. Not even the most confirmed sceptic can deny that we see and hear at a greater distance and command greater forces and speeds than an earlier generation; while it is equally certain that this progress is an enduring increase of knowledge, which is in no danger of being described as an error and rejected at any future date.

Secondly, it is a very striking fact that the impulse towards simplification and improvement of the world-picture of Physics was due in each instance to some kind of novel observation— that is, to some event in the world of sense. But at the same moment the structure of this physical world consistently moved farther and farther away from the world of sense and lost its former anthropomorphic character. Still further, physical sensations have been progressively eliminated, as for example in physical optics, in which the human eye no longer plays any part at all. Thus the physical world has become progressively more and more abstract; purely formal mathematical operations play a growing part, while qualitative differences tend to be explained more and more by means of quantitative differences.

Now we have already pointed out that the physical view of the world has been continually perfected and also related to the world of sense. If this fact is added to those mentioned in the last paragraph, the result is extraordinarily striking; at first, indeed, it appears completely paradoxical. Of this apparent paradox there is, in my opinion, only one rational explanation. This consists in saying that as the view of the physical world is perfected, it simultaneously recedes from the world of sense; and this process is tantamount to an approach to the world of reality. I have no logical proof on which to base this opinion; it is impossible to demonstrate the existence of the real world by purely rational methods: but at the same time it is equally impossible ever to refute it by logical methods. The final decision must rest upon a common-sense view of the world, and the old maxim still remains true that that world-view is the best which is the most fruitful. Physics would occupy an exceptional position among all the other sciences if it did not recognize the rule that the most far-reaching and valuable results of investigation can only be obtained by following a road leading to a goal which is theoretically unobtainable. This goal is the apprehension of true reality.

§ 2

What changes have taken place in the physical view of the world during the last twenty years? We all know that the changes which have occurred during this period are among the most profound that have ever arisen in the evolution of any science; we also know that the process of change has not yet come to an end. Nevertheless it would appear that in this flux of change certain characteristic forms of the structure of this new world are beginning to crystallize; and it is certainly worth while to attempt a description of these forms, if only in order to suggest certain improvements.

If we compare the old theory with the new, we find that the process of tracing back all qualitative distinctions to quantitative distinctions has been advanced very considerably. All the various chemical phenomena, for example, have now been explained by numerical and spatial relations. According to the modern view there are no more than two ultimate substances, namely positive and negative electricity. Each of these consists of a number of minute particles, similar in nature and with similar charges of an opposite character; the positive particle is called the proton, the negative the electron. Every chemical atom that is electrically neutral consists of a number of protons cohering with one another, and of a similar number of electrons, some of which are firmly fixed to the protons, together with which they form the nucleus of the atom, while the rest revolve around the nucleus.

Thus the Hydrogen atom, the smallest of all,

has one proton for nucleus and one electron revolving round the nucleus; while the largest atom, Uranium, contains 238 protons and 238 electrons; but only 92 electrons revolve round the nucleus while the others are fixed in it. Between these two atoms lie all the other elements, with many kinds of different combinations. The chemical properties of an element depend, not on the total number of its protons or electrons, but on the number of revolving electrons, which yield the atomic number of the element.

Apart from this important advance, which is however merely the successful application of an idea first evolved many centuries ago, there are two completely new ideas which distinguish the modern conception of the world from its predecessor; these are the Theory of Relativity, and the Quantum Theory. It is these two ideas which are peculiarly characteristic of the new world of Physics. The fact that they appeared in science almost simultaneously is something of a coincidence; for their content, as well as their practical effect upon the structure of the physical view of the world, are entirely different.

The Theory of Relativity seemed at first to introduce a certain amount of confusion into the traditional ideas of Time and Space; in the long run, however, it has proved to be the completion and culmination of the structure of classical Physics. To express the positive result of the Special Theory of Relativity in a single word, it might be described as the fusion of Time and Space in one unitary concept. It is not, of course, asserted that Time and Space are absolutely similar in nature; their relation resembles that between a real number and an imaginary number, when these are combined together to form the unified concept of a complex number. Looked at in this way, Einstein's work for Physics closely resembles that of Gauss for Mathematics. We might further continue the comparison by saying that the transition from the Special to the General Theory of Relativity is the counter-part in Physics to the transition from linear functions to the general theory of functions in mathematics.

Few comparisons are entirely exact, and the present is no exception to the rule. At the same time it gives a good idea of the fact that the introduction of the Theory of Relativity into the physical view of the world is one of the most important steps towards conferring unity and completeness. This appears clearly in the results of the Theory of Relativity, especially in the fusing of momentum and energy, in the identification of the concept of mass with the concept of energy, of inertial with ponderable mass, and in the reduction of the laws of gravitation to Riemann's geometry.

Brief though these main outlines are, they contain a vast mass of new knowledge. The new ideas mentioned apply to all natural events great and small, beginning with radio-active atoms emanating waves and corpuscles, and ending with the movements of celestial bodies millions of light-years away.

The last word on the Theory of Relativity probably still remains to be said. Surprises may yet await us, especially when we consider that the problem of amalgamating Electrodynamics with Mechanics has not yet been definitely solved. Again, the cosmological implications of the Theory of Relativity have not yet been fully cleared up, the chief reason being that everything depends upon the question whether or not the matter of outer space possesses a finite density; this question has not yet been answered. But whatever reply is eventually given to these questions, nothing will alter the fact that the Principle of Relativity has advanced the classical physical theory to its highest stage of completion, and that its world-view is rounded off in a very satisfactory manner.

This fact will perhaps be a sufficient reason for devoting no more time to the Theory of Relativity; I might also point out that there are many treatises on the Theory adapted to the requirements of readers of every kind.

§ 3

The idea of the universe as thus far described appeared almost perfectly adapted to its purpose; but this state of affairs has suddenly been upset by the Quantum Theory. Here again I shall attempt to describe the characteristic idea of this hypothesis in one word. We may say, then, that its essence consists in the fact that it introduces a new and universal constant, namely the elementary Quantum of Action. It was this constant which, like a new and mysterious messenger from the real world, insisted on turning up in every kind of measurement, and continued to claim a place for itself. On the other hand, it seemed so incompatible with the traditional view of the universe provided by Physics that it eventually destroyed the framework of this older view.

For a time it seemed that a complete collapse of classical Physics was not beyond the bounds of possibility; gradually however it appeared, as had been confidently expected by all who believed in the steady advance of science, that the introduction of the Quantum Theory led not to the destruction of Physics, but to a somewhat profound reconstruction, in the course of which the whole science was rendered more universal. For if the Quantum of Action is assumed to be infinitely small, Quantum Physics becomes merged in classical Physics. In fact the foundations of the structure of classical Physics not only proved unshakable, but actually were rendered firmer through the incorporation of the new ideas. The best course, therefore, will be first to examine the latter.

It will be best to begin by enumerating the essential component features. These are the universal constants, e.g. the gravitational constant, the velocity of light, the mass and charge of electrons and protons. These are perhaps the most tangible symbols of a real world, and they retain their meaning unchanged in the new view of the universe. Further, we may mention the great principles of the conservation of energy and of momentum, which, although they were under suspicion for a time, have eventually emerged unimpaired. It should be emphasized that in this process of transition these principles were proved to be something more than mere definitions, as some members of the Axiomatic School would like to believe. Further, we may mention the main laws of thermodynamics, and especially the second law, which through the introduction of an absolute value for entropy obtained a more exact formulation than it possessed in classical Physics. Lastly we may point to the Principle of Relativity, which has proved itself a reliable and eloquent guide in the new regions of Quantum Physics.

The question may now be asked whether modern Physics differs at all from the older Physics, if all these foundations of classical Physics have remained untouched. It is easy to find an answer to this question by examining the elementary Quantum of Action somewhat more closely. It implies that in principle an equation can be established between energy and frequency; $E = h\nu$.[1] It is this equation which

[1] In this equation E stands for Energy, and ν for Frequency, that is the number of vibrations per second.

classical Physics utterly fails to explain. The fact itself is so baffling because energy and frequency possess different dimensions; energy is a dynamic magnitude, whereas frequency is a kinematic magnitude. This fact in itself, however, does not contain a contradiction. The Quantum Theory postulates a direct connection between dynamics and kinematics; this connection is due to the fact that the unit of energy, and consequently the unit of mass, are based upon the units of length and of time; thus the connection, so far from being a contradiction, enriches and rounds off the classical theory. There is, nevertheless, a direct contradiction, which renders the new theory incompatible with the classical theory. The following considerations make clear this contradiction. Frequency is a local magnitude, and has a definite meaning only for a certain point in space; this is true alike of mechanical, electric and magnetic vibrations, so that all that is requisite is to observe the point in question for a sufficient time. Energy on the other hand

For example, light vibrations range from about 400 million million per second to about 800 million million. h represents "Planck's Constant", discovered by the author of this work. It is an unchanging or invariable quantity, and extremely minute, its value being 655 preceded by 26 decimal places. [TRANS.]

is an additive quantity; so that according to the classical theory it is meaningless to speak of energy at a certain point, since it is essential to state the physical system the energy of which is under discussion; just as it is similarly impossible to speak of a definite velocity unless the system be indicated to which velocity is referred. Now we are at liberty to choose whatever physical system we please, either little or great; and consequently the value of the energy is always to a certain extent arbitrary. The difficulty, then, consists in the fact that this arbitrary energy is supposed to be equated with a localized frequency. The gulf between these two concepts should now be clearly apparent: and in order to bridge this gulf a step of fundamental importance must be taken. This step does imply a break with those assumptions which classical Physics has always regarded and employed as axiomatic.

Hitherto it had been believed that the only kind of causality with which any system of Physics could operate was one in which all the events of the physical world—by which, as usual, I mean not the real world but the world-view of Physics—might be explained as being composed of local events taking place in a number of

individual and infinitely small parts of Space.
It was further believed that each of these elementary events was completely determined by
a set of laws without respect to the other events;
and was determined exclusively by the local
events in its immediate temporal and spatial
vicinity. Let us take a concrete instance of
sufficiently general application. We will assume
that the physical system under consideration
consists of a system of particles, moving in a
conservative field of force of constant total
energy. Then according to classical Physics each
individual particle at any time is in a definite
state; that is, it has a definite position and a
definite velocity, and its movement can be
calculated with perfect exactness from its initial
state and from the local properties of the field
of force in those parts of Space through which
the particle passes in the course of its movement.
If these data are known, we need know nothing
else about the remaining properties of the system
of particles under consideration.

In modern mechanics matters are wholly
different. According to modern mechanics, merely
local relations are no more sufficient for the
formulation of the law of motion than would
be the microscopic investigation of the different

parts of a picture in order to make clear its meaning. On the contrary, it is impossible to obtain an adequate version of the laws for which we are looking, unless the physical system is regarded *as a Whole*. According to modern mechanics, each individual particle of the system, in a certain sense, at any one time, exists simultaneously in every part of the space occupied by the system. This simultaneous existence applies not merely to the field of force with which it is surrounded, but also to its mass and its charge.

Thus we see that nothing less is at stake here than the concept of the particle—the most elementary concept of classical mechanics. We are compelled to give up the earlier essential meaning of this idea; only in a number of special borderline cases can we retain it. But if we pursue the line of thought indicated above, we shall find what it is that we can substitute for the concept of the particle in more general cases.

[*The following brief section may be omitted by readers not interested in the somewhat technical issues, and the subject resumed on p.* 38.]

[The Quantum Theory postulates that an equation subsists between energy and frequency. If this postulate is to have an unambiguous meaning, that is a meaning independent of the particular system to which it is referred, then the Principle of Relativity demands that a momentum vector[1] shall be equivalent to a wave-member vector; in other words, the absolute quantity of the momentum must be equivalent to the reciprocal of the length of a wave whose normal coincides with the direction of momentum. The wave in question must not be imagined as existing in ordinary three-dimensional space, but in so-called configuration space, the dimension of which is given by the number of degrees of freedom of the system, and in which the square of the element of length is measured by twice the kinetic energy; or what comes to the same thing, by the square of the total momentum. It thus appears that the wave-length follows from the kinetic energy, that is from the difference between the constant total energy and the potential energy; this difference must be regarded as a function of position given beforehand.

The product of the frequency and the wave-length gives us the rate of propagation of the wave; in other words, it gives us the phase-velocity of a given wave—the so-called material

[1] A vector is a quantity which has a definite direction; for example, "100 miles per hour East" (or any other direction) is a vector. [Trans.]

wave—in configuration space. If the appropriate
values are substituted in the familiar equation
of classical mechanics, we obtain the linear
homogeneous partial differential equation set
up by Schrödinger. This equation has provided
the basis of modern Quantum-mechanics, in
which it seems to play the same part as do the
equations established by Newton, Lagrange and
Hamilton in classical mechanics. Nevertheless
there is an important distinction between these
equations, consisting in the fact that in the latter
equations the co-ordinates of the configuration
point are not functions of time, but independent
variables. Accordingly, while for any given system
the classical equations of motion were more or
less numerous and corresponded to the number
of degrees of freedom of the system, there can
be only one single quantum-equation for each
system. In course of time the configuration point
of classical theory describes a definite curve; on
the other hand, the configuration point of the
material wave fills at any given time the whole
of infinite space, including those parts of space
where potential energy is greater than the total
energy, so that according to the classical theory,
kinetic energy would become negative in these
parts of space, and the momentum imaginary.

This case resembles the so-called total reflection of light, where according to geometrical optics light is completely reflected, because the angle of refraction becomes imaginary; whereas according to the wave-theory of light, it is perfectly possible for light to penetrate into the second medium, even if it cannot do so as a plane wave.

At the same time, the fact that there are points in configuration space where the potential energy exceeds the total energy is of extreme importance for Quantum-mechanics. Calculation shows that in every such instance a finite wave corresponds not to any given value of the energy constant, but corresponds only to certain definite values:—the so-called characteristic energy-values, which can be calculated from the wave-equation and have different values according to the nature of the given potential energy.

From the discrete characteristic energy-values, discrete characteristic values of the period of oscillation may be derived. The latter are determined according to the Quantum postulate, in a similar manner to that of a stretched cord with fixed ends; with this distinction that the latter quantization is determined by an external condition, viz. the length of the cord, whereas in the present instance it depends upon the

Quantum of Action, which in turn depends directly upon the differential equation.

To each characteristic vibration there corresponds a particular wave-function (ψ); this is the solution of the wave-equation; and all these different characteristic functions form the component elements for the description of any movement in terms of wave-mechanics.

Thus we reach the following result: in classical Physics the physical system under consideration is divided spatially into a number of smallest parts; by this means the motion of material bodies is traced back to the motion of their component particles, the latter being assumed to be unchangeable. In other words, the explanation is based upon a theory of corpuscles. Quantum Physics, on the other hand, analyses all motion into individual and periodic material waves, which are taken to correspond to the characteristic vibrations and characteristic functions of the system in question; in this way it is based upon wave-mechanics. Accordingly, in classical mechanics the simplest motion is that of an individual particle, whereas in quantum-mechanics the simplest motion is that of a simple periodic wave; according to the first, the entire motion of a body is taken as being the totality of the motions of its component particles; whereas according to the second, it consists in the joint effect of all kinds of periodic material waves. To illustrate the difference between these two views, we may once more refer to the vibrations of a stretched cord. On the one hand these vibrations may be imagined as consisting of the sum of the motions of the different particles of the cord, where each particle is in motion independently of all the rest and in accordance with the force acting upon it, which in turn depends upon the local curvature of the cord. On the other hand the process of vibration may be analysed into the fundamental and upper partial vibrations of the cord, where each vibration affects the cord in its totality and the sum total of vibration is the most general kind of motion taking place in the cord.

Wave-mechanics also furnishes an explanation for another fact which hitherto has been inexplicable. According to Niels Bohr's theory, the electrons of an atom move around the nucleus in accordance with laws very similar to those which govern the motion of the planets around the sun. Here the place of gravitation is taken by the attraction between the opposite charges of the nucleus and the electrons. There is, however, a curious distinction, consisting in the fact that the electrons can move only in definite orbits distinct from each other, whereas with the planets no one orbit appears to be privileged beyond any other. According to the wave theory of electrons this circumstance, at first sight unintelligible, is easily explained. If the orbit of an electron returns upon itself, it is clear that it must comprise an integral number of wavelengths, just as the length of a chain which forms a complete circle, if it consists of a number of equal links, must always equal an integral number of link-lengths. According to this view the revolution of an electron around the nucleus is not so much like the movement of a planet around the sun, as like the rotation of a symmetrical ring upon its centre, so that the ring as a whole retains the same position in space; thus there is no physical meaning in referring to the local position of the electron at any instant.

The following question may now be asked: if motion is to be analysed not into particles, but into material waves, what is the procedure of wave-mechanics when it is called upon to describe the motion of a single particle which occupies a given position at a given time? The answer to this question throws light upon the great contrast between the two theories with which we have been dealing. In the first instance we must examine the physical meaning of the wave function ψ of a simple periodic material wave. This meaning can be derived from the consideration that the energy of a material wave has a twofold meaning. It is true that it denotes the period of vibration of the wave; but of course it does not follow from this that it has lost its original meaning, which it derives from the principle of conservation of energy. But if the energy principle is to apply to wave-mechanics, then it must be possible to represent the energy of a material wave, not only by the frequency of its vibrations, but also by means of an integral comprehending the entire configuration space of the wave.

In fact, then, if the wave-equation is multiplied by $\bar{\psi}$ and the product is integrated over the entire configuration space, there results a definite expression for the energy, which can be most vividly interpreted in the following manner.

We imagine the material system of particles under consideration to be multiplied many times, and we further imagine that each of the resulting systems is in a different configuration, so that we obtain a very great number of particles in configuration space. We further allot to the configuration points existing in the different infinitely small elements of space a definite energy which is composed (*a*) of the value of the local potential energy (which is given beforehand) and (*b*) of a second element which varies as the square of the local gradient of ψ, and which we can interpret as being equivalent to kinetic energy. If, then, the spatial density of the configuration points at any one place is assumed to be equal to the square of the absolute value of ψ (which latter we may assume to have any magnitude we desire, since one of the constant factors of ψ can be selected by ourselves at will), it follows that the mean energy of all the configuration points is equivalent to the energy of the material wave. Accordingly the absolute value of the amplitude of the wave has no meaning whatever in a physical sense. If we imagine ψ to be selected in such a way that the square of the absolute value of ψ, when integrated over the configuration space, gives us the value 1, then we can also say that this square denotes the probability that the material system of particles is actually existing at the point in question within the configuration space. Thus we have found a vivid expression for the physical meaning of the wave-function ψ, which we were looking for.

In the course of all these considerations we had assumed that ψ had a definite characteristic function of its own, and that there was a simple periodic wave corresponding to it. Similar statements, however, may be made for the general case where waves having different periods are superimposed. In that case the wave-function ψ is the algebraic sum of the periodic characteristic functions multiplied by a certain amplitude constant, and once again the square of the absolute value of ψ denotes the probability for the corresponding position of the configuration point. In the general case, of course, we can no longer speak of one single definite period of vibration of the material waves; on the other hand, however, we can still speak of a definite energy. Accordingly the Quantum-equation $E = h\nu$ loses its original meaning and only gives us an average frequency ν. It is worth noting here that if a sufficiently large number of different waves having approximately equal frequencies are superimposed, the wave-function of the resulting wave is the sum of the individual wave-functions; its energy on the other hand does not increase proportionately with the number of individual waves, but

always retains its original mean value; the
energy of a group of individual waves defines
a mean frequency, and similarly the momentum
of this group serves to define a mean wave-length.

To begin with, the amplitudes and phases of
the individual waves can be selected at will.
Beyond this, however, it is impossible to introduce further variety into the mechanical processes
of which wave-mechanics can provide instances.
This fact becomes important when we turn to
the question raised above, in which we ask how
the motion of a single definite particle is to be
described in terms of wave-mechanics. It appears
immediately that *such a description cannot be
made in any exact sense*. Wave-mechanics possesses
only one means of defining the position of a
particle, or more generally the position of a
definite point in configuration space; this consists
in superimposing a group of individual waves of
the system, in such a manner that their wave-
functions cancel each other by interference everywhere within configuration space, and intensify
each other only at the one point in question. In
this case the probability of all the other configuration points would be equal to O, and would
be equal to 1 only for the one point in question.
In order to isolate this point completely we

should, however, require infinitely small wave-lengths, and consequently infinitely great momentum. Therefore, in order to obtain a result which would be even approximately useful, we should have to begin by substituting for the definite configuration point a finite (though still small) region of configuration space, or so-called wave-group; this sufficiently expresses the fact that ascertaining the position of a configuration point is always in the wave theory affected by some sort of uncertainty.

If we wish to go further and ascribe to the system of particles a definite quantity of momentum as well as a definite configuration, then the Quantum postulate, if taken strictly, will allow us to make use of only one single wave of a definite length for our exposition, and once more description becomes impossible. On the other hand, if a slight uncertainty is allowed to creep into the quantity of momentum, then we can reach our goal, at least approximately, if we make use of the wave within a certain narrow range of frequency.

According to wave-mechanics, both the position and the momentum of a system of particles can never be defined without some uncertainty. Now the fact is that between these two kinds of uncertainty there is a definite relation. This follows from the simple reflection that if the waves of which we make use are to cancel each other through interference outside the above-mentioned small configuration region, then in spite of their small difference in frequency, noticeable differences in propagation must appear at the opposite boundaries of the region. If in accordance with the Quantum postulate, we substitute differences of momentum for differences of propagation, we obtain Heisenberg's Principle, which states that the product of the uncertainty of position and uncertainty of momentum is at least of the same order of magnitude as the quantum of action.]

The more accurately the position of the configuration point is ascertained, the less accurate is the amount of momentum; and conversely. These two kinds of uncertainty are thus in a certain sense complementary; this complementariness is limited by the fact that momentum can under certain conditions be defined with absolute accuracy in wave-mechanics, whereas the position of a configuration point always remains uncertain within a finite region.

Now this relation of uncertainty, established

by Heisenberg, is something quite unheard of in classical mechanics. It had always been known, of course, that every measurement is subject to a certain amount of inaccuracy; but it had always been assumed that an improvement in method would lead to an improvement in accuracy, and that this process could be carried on indefinitely. According to Heisenberg, however, there is a definite limit to the accuracy obtainable. What is most curious is that this limit does not affect position and velocity separately, but only the two when combined together. In principle, either taken by itself can be measured with absolute accuracy, but only at the cost of the accuracy of the other.

Strange as this assertion may seem, it is definitely established by a variety of facts. I will give one example to illustrate this. The most direct and accurate means of ascertaining the position of a particle consists in the optical method, when the particle is looked at with the naked eye or through a microscope, or else is photographed. Now for this purpose the particle in question must be illuminated. If this is done the definition becomes more accurate; consequently the measurement becomes more exact in proportion as the light-waves employed become shorter and shorter. In this sense, then, any desired degree of accuracy can be attained. On the other hand there is also a disadvantage, which affects the measurement of velocity. Where the masses in question have a certain magnitude, the effect of light upon the illuminated object may be disregarded. But the case is altered if a very small mass, e.g. a single electron, is selected; because each ray of light, which strikes the electron and is reflected by it, gives it a distinct impulse; and the shorter the light-wave the more powerful is this impulse. Consequently, the shorter the light-wave the more accurately is it possible to determine position; but at the same moment measurement of velocity becomes proportionately inaccurate; and similarly in analogous instances.

On the view which has just been set out classical mechanics, which is based on the assumption of unchanging and accurately measurable corpuscles moving with a definite velocity, forms one ideal limiting case. This ideal case is actually realized when the observed system possesses a relatively considerable energy. When this happens, the distinct characteristic energy values will lie close to each other, and a relatively small region of energy will contain a considerable number of

high wave-frequencies (i.e. of short wave-lengths);
through the superposition of these a small wave-
group with definite momentum can be delimited
comparatively accurately within the configuration
space. In this case, wave-mechanics merges with
the mechanics of particles; Schrödinger's differential equation becomes the classical differential
equation of Hamilton and Jacobi, and the wave-
group travels in configuration space in accordance with the same laws which govern the motion
of a system of particles according to classical
mechanics. But this state of affairs is of a limited
duration; for the individual material waves are
not interfering continually in the same manner,
and consequently the wave-group will disintegrate
more or less quickly; the position of the relative configuration point will become more and
more uncertain, and finally the only quantity
remaining that is accurately defined is the wave-
function ψ.

The question now arises whether these conclusions correspond with experience. Since the
Quantum of Action is so small, this question can
be answered only within the framework of atomic
physics; consequently the methods employed will
always be extremely delicate. At present we can
only say that hitherto no fact has been discovered

which throws doubt on the applicability in Physics of all these conclusions.

The fact is that since the wave-equation was first formulated, the theory has been developing at a most remarkable rate. It is impossible within the framework of a small volume to mention all the extensions and applications of the theory which have been evolved within recent years. I shall confine myself to the so-called stress of protons and electrons; the formulation of Quantum-mechanics in terms of Relativity; the application of the theory to molecular problems, and the treatment of the so-called "many-body problem", i.e. its application to a system containing a number of exactly similar particles. Here statistical questions, relating to the number of possible states within a system, having a given energy, are particularly important; they also have a bearing on the calculation of the entropy of the system.

Finally, I cannot here enter in detail upon the Physics of light-quanta. In a certain sense this study has developed in the opposite direction from the Physics of particles. Originally Maxwell's theory of electromagnetic waves dominated this region, and it was not seen until later that we must assume the existence of discrete light-particles; in other words that the electromagnetic waves, like the material waves, must be interpreted as waves of probability.

Perhaps there is no more impressive proof of the fact that a pure wave theory cannot satisfy the demands of modern Physics any more than a pure corpuscular theory. Both theories, in fact, represent extreme limiting cases. The corpuscular theory, which is the basis of classical mechanics, does justice to the configuration of a system, but fails to determine the values of its energy and of momentum; conversely the wave theory, which is characteristic of classical electrodynamics, can give an account of energy and momentum, but excludes the idea of the localization of light-particles. The standard case is represented by the intermediate region, where both theories play equally important parts; this region can be approached from either side, although at present a close approach is impossible. Here many obscure points await solution, and it remains to be seen which of the various methods employed for their solution best leads to the goal. Among them we may mention the matrix calculus invented by Heisenberg, Born, and Jordan, the wave theory due to de Broglie and Schrödinger, and the mathematics of the q numbers introduced by Dirac.

§ 4

If we attempt to draw a comprehensive conclusion from the above description and to obtain an insight into the distinguishing characteristics of our new picture of the world, the first impression will no doubt be somewhat unsatisfactory. First of all it will appear surprising that wave-mechanics, which itself is in complete contradiction to classical mechanics, nevertheless makes use of concepts drawn from the classical corpuscular theory; e.g. the concept of the co-ordinates and momentum of a particle, and of the kinetic and potential energy of a system of particles. The contradiction is the more surprising since it afterwards proved impossible simultaneously to determine exactly the position and momentum of a particle. At the same time these concepts are absolutely essential to wave-mechanics; for without them it would be impossible to define configuration space and ascertain its measurements.

There is another difficulty attached to the wave theory, consisting in the fact that material waves are not as easy to bring before the imagination as are acoustic or electromagnetic waves; for they exist in configuration space instead of ordinary space, and their period of vibration depends on the choice of the physical system to which they belong. The more extensive this system is assumed to be, the greater will be its energy, and with this the frequency.

It must be admitted that these are serious difficulties. It will be possible, however, to overcome them if two conditions are fulfilled:—the new theory must be free from internal contradictions; and its applied results must be definite and of some significance for measurement. At the present time opinions are somewhat divided whether these requirements are fulfilled by Quantum-mechanics, and if so, to what extent. For this reason I propose to discuss this fundamental point further.

It has frequently been pointed out that Quantum-mechanics confines itself on principle to magnitudes and quantities which can be observed, and to questions which have a meaning within the sphere of Physics. This observation is correct; but in itself it must not be considered a special advantage of the Quantum Theory as opposed to other theories. For the question whether a physical magnitude can in principle be observed, or whether a certain question has a meaning as applied to Physics, can never be answered *a priori*, but only from the standpoint of a given

theory. The distinction between the different
theories consists precisely in the fact that
according to one theory a certain magnitude can
in principle be observed, and a certain question
have a meaning as applied to Physics; while
according to the other theory this is not the
case. For example, according to the theories of
Fresnel and Lorentz, with their assumption of
a stationary ether, the absolute velocity of the
earth can in principle be observed; but according
to the Theory of Relativity it cannot; again, the
absolute acceleration of a body can be in principle observed according to Newtonian mechanics,
but according to Relativity mechanics it cannot.
Similarly the problem of the construction of a
perpetuum mobile had a meaning before the
principle of the conservation of energy was
introduced, but ceased to have a meaning after
its introduction. The choice between these two
opposed theories depends not upon the nature
of the theories in themselves, but upon experience. Hence it is not sufficient to describe the
superiority of Quantum-mechanics, as opposed
to classical mechanics, by saying that it confines
itself to quantities and magnitudes which can in
principle be observed, for in its own way this is
true of the classical mechanics. We must indicate

the particular magnitudes or quantities which, according to Quantum-mechanics, are or are not in principle observed; after this has been done it remains to demonstrate that experience agrees with the assertion.

Now this demonstration has in fact been completed, e.g. with respect to Heisenberg's Principle of Uncertainty, so far as seems possible at the present moment, and to this extent it can be looked upon as proving the superiority of wave-mechanics.

In spite of these considerable successes, the Principle of Uncertainty which is characteristic of Quantum Physics has caused considerable hesitation, because the definition of magnitudes and quantities which are continually in use is in principle treated as being inexact by this theory. This dissatisfaction is increased by the fact that the concept of probability has been introduced in the interpretation of the equations used in Quantum-mechanics; for this seems to imply a surrender of the demands of strict causality in favour of a form of indeterminism. To-day, indeed, there are eminent physicists who under the compulsion of facts are inclined to sacrifice the principle of strict causality in the physical view of the world.

If such a step should actually prove necessary the goal of physicists would become more remote; and this would be a disadvantage whose importance it is impossible to overestimate. For in my opinion, so long as any choice remains, determinism is in all circumstances preferable to indeterminism, simply because a definite answer to a question is always preferable to an indefinite one.

So far as I can see, however, there is no ground for such a renunciation. For there always remains the possibility that the reason why it is impossible to give a definite answer resides, not in the nature of the theory, but in the manner in which the question is asked. If a question is inadequately formulated physically, the most perfect physical theory can give no definite answer; a fact widely known in classical statistics and frequently discussed. For example, if two elastic spheres strike one another in a plane, while their velocities before impact and the laws of impact are known in all their details, it still remains impossible to state their velocities after impact. The fact is that, in order to calculate the four unknown components of the velocities of the two spheres after impact, we have only three equations derived from the conservation of energy and the two components of momentum. From this, however, we do not infer that there is no causality governing impact phenomena; what we do say is that certain essential data are missing which are requisite for their complete determination.

In order to apply these considerations to the problems of Quantum Physics, we must now return to the arguments dealt with in the Introduction.

If it is really true that, in its perpetual changes, the structure of the physical world-view moves further and further away from the world of the senses, and correspondingly approaches the real world (which, as we saw, cannot in principle be apprehended at all), then it plainly follows that our view of the world must be purged progressively of all anthropomorphic elements. Consequently we have no right to admit into the physical world-view any concepts based in any way upon human mensuration. In fact this is not the case with Heisenberg's Principle of Uncertainty: this was reached from the consideration that the elements of the new view of the world are not material corpuscles, but simple periodic material waves which correspond to the physical system under consideration—a conclusion obtained in accordance with the mathematical principle that it is impossible to determine a definite particle with definite momentum by means of superposition of simple periodic waves having a finite length. The principle has nothing whatever to do with any measurement, while the material waves are definitely determined by means of the mathematical problem of boundary values relating to the case in question. Here there is no question of indeterminism.

The question of the relation between the material waves and the world of sense is a different one. For this relation renders it possible for us to become acquainted with physical events; if a system were completely cut off from its surroundings we could never know of its existence.

At first glance it appears that this question has nothing to do with Physics, since it belongs partly to Physiology and partly to Psychology. These objections, however, lead to no real difficulty. It is always possible to imagine suitably constructed instruments being substituted for human senses, e.g. self-registering apparatus like a sensitive film, which registers the impressions derived from the environment, and is thus capable of furnishing evidence about the events taking place in these surroundings. If such instruments are included within the physical system which we propose to consider, and if all other influences are eliminated, then we have a physical system cut off from the rest of the world of which we can discover something by means of measurement; although it is true that we must take into account the structure of the measuring instruments, and the reaction which they might conceivably have upon the events which we desire to measure.

If we possessed an instrument reacting to a simple periodic material wave in the same way as a resonator reacts to a sound-wave, then we would be in a position to measure individual material waves and thus to analyse their behaviour. This is not the case; the fact is that the indications given by such instruments as we possess, e.g. the darkening of a photographic film, do not allow us to make a safe inference about all the details of the process under examination. We have no right, however, to infer from this that the laws of material waves are indeterminate.

Another and more direct attempt might be made to substantiate the assumption of indeterminism from the fact that, according to wave-mechanics, the events within a system of particles cut off from the outside world are not determined

in any way by the initial state of the system,
i.e. by the initial configuration and initial momentum. There is not even an approximate determination; for the wave-group corresponding to
the initial state will in time disintegrate generally
and fall apart into individual waves of probability.

On closer consideration, however, we see that
in this instance the element of indeterminism is
due to the manner in which the question is asked.
The question is based upon corpuscular mechanics;
and in corpuscular mechanics the initial state
governs the course of the event for all time.
But in wave-mechanics such a question has no
place, if only because the final result is on principle affected with a finite inaccuracy due to the
Principle of Uncertainty.

Since the times of Leibniz, on the other hand,
another form of question in classical mechanics
has been known which in this sphere leads to a
definite answer. An event is completely determined for all time if, apart from the configuration
at a certain time, we know, not the momentum,
but the configuration of the same system at a
different instant. In this case the principle of
variation, or principle of least action, is used in
order to calculate the event. To take the previous
example, where two elastic spheres meet in a

plane, if we know the initial and final position of the spheres and the interval between those two positions, then the three unknown quantities, namely the two local co-ordinates and the time co-ordinate of impact, are completely determined by the three equations of conservation.

This changed formulation of the problem differs from the previous formulation because it is immediately applicable to wave-mechanics. It is true, as we saw, that a given configuration can never be defined with complete accuracy by the wave theory; but on the other hand it is theoretically possible to reduce the uncertainty below any desired limit, and thus to determine the event in question with any desired degree of accuracy. Further, the disintegration of wave-groups is no evidence in favour of indeterminism, since it is equally possible for a wave-group to conglomerate: in both the wave theory and the corpuscular theory the *direction* of the process is immaterial. Any movement might equally well take place in the opposite direction.

When the above formulation of the problem is adopted a given wave-group generally, of course, exists only at the two selected instants: in the intervening period, as well as before and after the process, the different elementary waves will exist separately. But whether they are described as material waves or as waves of probability, in either case they will be completely determined. This is the explanation of the apparent paradox, that when a physical system passes by a definite process from one definite configuration during a definite time into some other definite configuration, the question what its configurations are during the intervening period has no physical significance; similarly on this view there is no meaning in the question of what is the track of light quantum emitted from a point source and absorbed at a given point on an observation-screen.

It should at the same time be emphasized that on this view the meaning of determinism is not exactly what it is in classical Physics. In the latter the configuration is determined; in Quantum Physics, the material waves. The distinction is important, because the connection between the configuration and the world of sense is far more direct than that between the material waves and the sense-world. To this extent the relation between the physical world-view and the world of sense appears to be considerably looser in modern Physics.

This is undoubtedly a disadvantage; but it

is the price that must be paid in order to preserve the determinism of our world-view. And
further, this step appears to lie in the general
direction in which Physics is actually developing;
this has been pointed out on more than one
occasion, since in the course of its progressive
evolution, the structure of the physical view of
the world is moving farther and farther away
from the world of sense, and assuming more and
more abstract forms. Indeed, the principle of
Relativity seems actually to demand such a
view; for on this principle Time stands on the
same level with Space, whence it follows that, if
a finite space is required for the causal description
of a physical process, a finite temporal interval
must also be used in order to complete the
description.

On the other hand, it may well be that the
suggested formulation of the question is too
one-sided, and too anthropomorphic to furnish
satisfactory material for a new theory of the
structure of the physical world; it may be that
we shall have to look for some other formulation.
In any case many complex problems remain to
be solved, and many obscure points to be
cleared up.

In view of the peculiar difficulties of the

position which has been reached by theoretical Physics, a feeling of doubt persists whether the theory, with all its radical innovations, is really on the right path. The answer to this decisive question depends wholly upon the degree of necessary contact with the sense world which the physical world-view maintains in the course of its incessant advance. If this contact is lost even the most perfect world-view would be no better than a bubble ready to burst at the first puff of wind. There is, fortunately, no cause for apprehension, at least in this respect: indeed we may assert without exaggeration that there was no period in the history of Physics when theory and experience were linked so closely together as they are now. Conversely, it was the facts learned from experiments that shook and finally overthrew the classical theory. Each new idea and each new step were suggested to investigators, where it was not actually thrust upon them, as the result of measurements. The Theory of Relativity was led up to by Michelson's experiments on optical interference, and the Quantum Theory by Lummer's, Pringsheim's, Ruben's and Kurlbaum's measurements of the spectral distribution of energy, by Lenard's experiments on the photoelectric effect, and by Franck and

Hertz's experiments on the impact of electrons. It would lead me too far if I were to enter on the numerous and surprising results which have compelled Physical theory to abandon the classical standpoint and to enter on a definite new course.

We can only hope that no change will take place in this peaceful international collaboration. It is in this reciprocal action of experiment and theory—which is at once a stimulus to and a check upon progress—that we see the surest and indeed the only guarantee of the future advance of Physics.

What will be the ultimate goal? I had occasion at the beginning to point out that research in general has a twofold aim—the effective domination of the world of sense, and the complete understanding of the real world; and that both these aims are in principle unattainable. But it would be a mistake to be discouraged on this account. Both our theoretical and practical tangible results are too great to warrant discouragement; and every day adds to them. Indeed, there is perhaps some justification for seeing in the very fact that this goal is unattainable, and the struggle unending, a blessing for the human mind in its search after knowledge. For it is in this way that

its two noblest impulses—enthusiasm and reverence—are preserved and inspired anew.

§ 5

What now do we mean by physical law? A
physical law is any proposition enunciating a
fixed and absolutely valid connection between
measurable physical quantities—a connection
which permits us to calculate one of these quantities if the others have been discovered by
measurement. The highest and most keenly
desired aim of any physicist is to obtain the
most perfect possible knowledge of the laws of
Physics, whether he looks at them from a utili-
tarian point of view and values them because
they enable him to save himself the trouble of
costly measurements, or takes a deeper view and
looks to them for satisfaction of a profound
yearning after knowledge and for a firm basis
of natural science.

How do we discover the individual laws of
Physics, and what is their nature? It should be
remarked, to begin with, that we have no right
to assume that any physical laws exist, or if they
have existed up to now, that they will continue

to exist in a similar manner in future. It is perfectly conceivable that one fine day Nature should cause an unexpected event to occur which would baffle us all; and if this were to happen we would be powerless to make any objection, even if the result would be that, in spite of our endeavours, we should fail to introduce order into the resulting confusion. In such an event, the only course open to science would be to declare itself bankrupt. For this reason, science is compelled to begin by the general assumption that a general rule of law dominates throughout Nature, or, in Kantian terminology, to treat the concept of causality as being one of the categories which are given *a priori* and without which no kind of knowledge can be attained.

From this it follows that the nature of the laws of Physics, and the content of these laws, cannot be obtained by pure thought; the only possible method is to turn to the investigation of Nature, to collect the greatest possible mass of varied experiences, to compare these and to generalize them in the simplest and most comprehensive proposition. In other words, we must have recourse to the method of induction.

The content of an experience is proportionally richer as the measurements upon which it is based are more exact. Hence it is obvious that the advance of physical knowledge is closely bound up with the accuracy of physical instruments and with the technique of measurement. The latest developments of Physics provide us with striking examples of the truth of this. Measurement alone, however, does not suffice. For each measurement is an individual event standing by itself; as such, it is determined by special circumstances, especially by a definite place and a definite time, but also by a definite measuring instrument, and by a definite observer. It is true that frequently the generalization which is our object is quite obvious and, so to speak, thrusts itself upon us; on the other hand, there are cases where it is extremely difficult to find the common law governing a number of different measurements, either because it seems impossible to find such a law, or because a number of different laws seem available in order to generalize the facts. Both possibilities are equally unsatisfactory.

In such cases, the only method of advance consists in introducing a so-called working hypothesis to see what it is worth and how far it will lead. It is generally a sign that the hypothesis is likely to turn out useful if it works even in those regions for which it was not originally designed. In such a case we have a right to assume that the law which it enunciates has a deeper meaning and opens the way to unmistakably new knowledge.

We see, then, that a good working hypothesis is essential for inductive investigation. This being so, we are faced with the difficult question how we are to set about to find the most suitable hypothesis. For this there can be no general rule. Logical thought by itself does not suffice—not even where it has an exceptionally large and manifold body of experience to aid it. The only possible method consists in immediately gripping the problem or in seizing upon some happy idea. Such an intellectual leap can be executed only by a lively and independent imagination and by a strong creative power, guided by an exact knowledge of the given facts so that it follows the right path.

Such an intellectual process generally consists in the introduction of certain mental images and analogies which point the way to the reigning laws already known in other regions, thus suggesting a further step towards the simplification of the physical view of the world.

It is precisely at these points where success

seems to be awaiting us, however, that a serious danger is frequently hidden. Once a step forward has succeeded and the working hypothesis has demonstrated its usefulness, we must go further. We have to reach the actual essence of the hypothesis and, by suitably formulating it, we have to throw light upon its genuine content by eliminating everything that is inessential. This process is not as simple as it might appear. The intellectual leap of which we spoke above constructs a kind of bridge by which we can approach fresh knowledge; but on closer examination it frequently appears that this bridge is merely provisional, and that a more enduring structure must be put in its place, capable of bearing the heavy artillery of critical logic.

We must bear in mind that every hypothesis is the outcome of the efforts of imagination, and that imagination works through direct intuition. But in Physics, as soon as we come to look for a rational theory or a logical demonstration, direct intuition is a very doubtful ally, however indispensable it may be while we are forming our hypothesis. For while it is natural that we should rely upon imaginations and ideas of this kind, which proved fruitful in one direction or another such reliance is only too apt to lead to an overestimation of their importance and to untenable generalizations. We must further recognize that the authors of a new and practicable theory are frequently little inclined to introduce any important changes in the groups of ideas which led them towards their discoveries, whether from indolence or from a certain sentimental feeling, and that they often exert the whole of their well-earned authority in order to be able to maintain their original standpoint. Thus we shall readily understand the difficulties which often stand in the way of healthy theoretical development. Examples may be found at every point in the history of Physics, and I propose to enumerate some of the more important of them.

The first exact measurements were made in the region of Space and Time—the first region where accurate measurement was possible. Hence naturally the earliest physical laws were discovered in this field; in other words, in the sphere of mechanics. Again, we can readily understand how it came about that the first laws which were established related to those motions which occur regularly and independently of external interference, namely, the motions of the celestial bodies. We know that the civilized peoples of the

East had discovered thousands of years ago how to derive from their observations formulæ which allowed them to calculate in advance the motion of the sun and the planets with great accuracy. Each improvement in the instruments of measurement was accompanied by an improvement of the formulæ. By their co-ordination and comparison the theories of Ptolemy, Copernicus and Kepler were evolved in course of time, each of which is simpler and more exact than those which preceded it. All these theories are alike in endeavouring to answer the question, what is the connection between the position of a celestial body, a planet for example, and the moment of time at which it occupies this position? The nature of this necessary connection is, of course, different for the different planets, and this in spite of the fact that the motions of the planets have many characteristics in common.

The decisive step beyond this type of question was taken by Newton. Newton summed up all the formulæ relating to the planets in one single law governing their motion, and indeed that of all the celestial bodies. He was enabled to do this because he made the law of motion independent of the particular moment to which it is applied: for the instant he substituted the time-differential. Newton's theory of planetary motion enunciates a fixed connection not between the position of a planet and time, but between the acceleration of a planet and its distance from the sun. Now this law—a vectorial differential equation—is the same for all the planets. Hence if the position and velocity of a planet are known for any moment, then its motion for all time can be exactly calculated.

The successes obtained as the result of the further application of Newton's formulation of the laws of motion prove that it is not merely a new description of certain natural phenomena, but that it represents a real advance in the understanding of actual facts. It is not merely more exact than Kepler's formulæ, for example when it allows for the interference in the elliptical orbit of the earth around the sun due to the periodic proximity of Jupiter, where formula and measurement are in exact agreement; more than that, it also covers the motion of such bodies as comets, twin stars, etc., which altogether elude Kepler's laws. The complete and immediate success of Newton's theory was due, however, to the fact that when applied to motion occurring on the earth, it led to the same numerical laws of gravitation and pendulum movements which

Galileo had already discovered by measurement, and also threw light on otherwise inexplicable phenomena, such as those of tides, rotation of the plane of the pendulum, precession of the axis of rotation, etc.

The question which especially interests us at the moment is how Newton reached his differential equation for planetary motion. He did not reach it by establishing a connection between the acceleration of a planet and its distance from the sun, and by looking for a numerical connection between them; what he did was first to forge an intellectual link between them, leading from the concept of the position of a planet to that of its acceleration; and this link he called Force. He assumed that the position of a planet relatively to the sun depends upon a force of attraction directed towards the sun, and that the same attractive force also causes a definite change in the planet's motion. This was the germ of the law of gravitation, as well as of the law of inertia. The notion of force was no doubt derived (as the word implies) from the idea of the muscular sensation which arises when a weight is lifted or a ball is thrown; this idea was generalized and applied to every kind of change of motion, even where the forces in question are so great that no human power could possibly suffice to effect them.

Small wonder, then, that Newton attributed the greatest importance to the concept of force which had helped him to reach such striking results. At the same time it must be noted that this concept does not occur in the law of motion proper. Newton looked to the concept of force for an explanation of every change of motion; and thus it came about that Newtonian force was regarded as the main and fundamental concept in mechanics, and not only in mechanics, but also in Physics; so that, in course of time, physicists formed the habit of making their first question when dealing with physical phenomena: what force is here in action?

Recent developments in Physics present a certain contrast with Newton's theory, so that in a manner it is true to say that the concept of force is no longer of fundamental importance for physical theory. In modern mechanics force is no more than a magnitude of secondary importance, and its place has been taken by higher and more comprehensive concepts—that of work[1] or

[1] "Work" is here used in its scientific sense of the product of the force and the distance through which the force acts. [TRANS.]

potential, where force in general is defined as a negative potential gradient.

It might here be objected that work surely cannot be looked upon as something primary, since there must be some kind of force in existence that does the work. This kind of argument is of the physiological and not of the physical order. It is true that in lifting a weight the contraction of the muscles and the accompanying sensations are primary, and are the cause of the motion which actually takes place. But this kind of work, which is a physiological process, must be clearly distinguished from the physical force of attraction with which alone we are here concerned; it is this force which the earth exerts upon everything having weight; and this in its turn depends upon the gravitational potential which is already in existence and is primary.

The idea of potential is superior to that of force, partly because it simplifies the laws of Physics, and also because the significance of the idea of potential has a far greater scope than that of force; it reaches beyond the sphere of mechanics into that of chemical affinities, where we are no longer concerned with Newtonian force. It must be admitted that the idea of potential has not the advantage of immediate obviousness which belongs to force by virtue of its anthropo-morphic quality; whence it follows that the elimination of the concept of force renders the laws of Physics much less obvious and easy of understanding. Yet this development is quite natural; the laws of Physics have no considera-tion for the human senses; they depend upon facts, and not upon the obviousness of facts.

In my opinion, the teaching of mechanics will still have to begin with Newtonian force, just as optics begins with the sensation of colour, and thermodynamics with the sensation of warmth, despite the fact that a more precise basis is sub-stituted later on. Again, it must not be forgotten that the significance of all physical concepts and propositions ultimately does depend on their relation to the human senses. This is indeed characteristic of the peculiar methods employed in physical research. If we wish to form concepts and hypotheses applicable to Physics, we must begin by having recourse to our powers of imagination; and these depend upon our specific sensations, which are the only source of all our ideas. But to obtain physical laws we must abstract exhaustively from the images intro-duced, and remove from the definitions set up all irrelevant elements and all imagery which do not stand in a logical connection with the measurements obtained. Once we have formulated physical laws, and reached definite conclusions by mathematical processes, the results which we have obtained must be translated back into the language of the world of our senses if they are to be of any use to us. In a manner this method is circular; but it is essential, for the simplicity and universality of the laws of Physics are revealed only after all anthropomorphic additions have been eliminated.

The concept of Force as used by Newton is only one of a number of intellectual links and auxiliary notions employed in order to render an idea more intelligible. In this connection I should like to mention the idea of osmotic pressure introduced by van't Hoff. This idea proved particularly fruitful in physical chemistry, where it was used in order to formulate the physical laws of solutions, especially of the freezing-point and steam-pressure. To obtain instances of osmotic pressure, and measure it accurately, is not altogether easy, since an extremely complex apparatus (the so-called semi-permeable membranes) is required. We must the more admire the intuitive insight which led van't Hoff to formulate the laws known under his name despite the scantiness of the observed facts at his disposal. Yet in their present form these laws require osmotic pressure no more than the laws of motion require Newtonian Force.

Besides the above there are other kinds of intellectual aids which assist imagination, and have proved of great assistance in the formation of working hypotheses, but which in the further course of development actually embarrassed later progress. One of these is particularly worth mention here. Men had accustomed themselves to see in some kind of force the cause underlying every natural change; and thus they were all the more disposed to imagine every invariable and constant magnitude or quantity as being of the nature of a *Substance*. From the earliest times the concept of Substance has played an important part in Physics: but closer examination shows that this has not always been helpful. It is, of course, easy to see that wherever conservation is concerned, it is possible to assume a Substance of which conservation is predicated; and such an assumption undoubtedly makes it easier to grasp the meaning of the principle, and hence facilitates its use. A magnitude which in spite of every change retains its quantity surely cannot be imagined more vividly than in the

shape of a moving material body. It is a feature
of this tendency that we are so prone to interpret
all natural events as being movements of masses
of substance—a mechanistic interpretation. For
example, the origin and distribution of light were
explained by wave-motion in a substantial light
ether; the chief laws of optics were described in
this manner and found to agree with experience
—until the moment came when the mechanistic
theory of Substance failed and became lost in
unfruitful speculation.

Again, for a time, the concept of Substance
proved exceedingly useful as applied to Heat.
The careful development of calorimetry, during
the first half of the last century, was due in the
main to the assumption that an unchanging
heat-substance flowed from the warmer into the
colder body. When it was shown that in these
circumstances the amount of heat can be increased
(e.g. by friction) the Substance theory defended
itself by appealing to supplementary hypotheses.
But although this method helped for some time,
it did not avail indefinitely.

In the theory of electricity the dangerous consequences of an exaggerated application of the
idea of Substance became obvious at an early
stage. Here again the idea of a subtle and quick-

moving electrical substance, giving rise to certain manifestations of force, serves admirably in order to render plastic before the mind such principles as that of the invariability of the quantity of electricity, and such subsidiary ideas as those of the electrical current and of the reciprocal action of charged conductors carrying a current. Here again, however, the analogy fails as soon as we have to allow for the fact that this view implies the assumption of the existence of two opposite substances, one positive and one negative, which completely neutralize each other when they are combined. Such an occurrence is at least as unthinkable as the creation of two opposite substances (in the usual sense) out of nothing.

In this way we see that imaginative ideas and their resultant viewpoints must be used with the greatest caution, even when they have proved their value for some length of time, and despite the fact that they are indispensable for physical investigation and have provided the key to new knowledge on innumerable occasions. There is only one sure guide towards further development, and that is measurement, together with any logical conclusions that can be drawn from the concepts attached to this method. All other conclusions, and especially those characterized by their so-called self-evidence, should always be looked upon with a certain suspicion. The validity of a proof dealing with well-defined concepts is to be judged by reason and not by intuition.

§ 6

Up to this point we have been considering the manner in which the knowledge of physical laws is obtained. We will now proceed to examine the content and the essential nature of the laws of Physics in somewhat greater detail.

A physical law is generally expressed in a mathematical formula, which permits us to calculate the temporal succession of the events taking place in a certain physical system under certain definite and given conditions. From this point of view all the laws of Physics can be divided into two main groups.

The first group consists of those laws which remain valid even when the time order is reversed; in other words, when every process that fulfils their requirements can take place in the reversed order without running counter to them. The laws of mechanics and of electrodynamics are of this nature, except in so far as they relate to chemical phenomena and the phenomena of heat. Every purely mechanical or electrodynamic process can take place in the reverse direction. The movement of a body falling without friction is accelerated in accordance with the same law which governs the retardation of a body rising without friction; the same laws govern the movement of a pendulum to the left and to the right, and a wave can travel equally well in any direction and in any sense; a planet could equally well revolve around the sun westwards as eastwards. The question whether such movements could actually be reversed, and if so under what conditions, is another matter which need not here be discussed: we are now dealing with the law as such, not with the particular facts to which it applies.

The laws belonging to the second group are characterized by the fact that their time order is of essential importance, so that the events taking place in accordance with these laws have only one temporal direction and cannot be reversed. Among these processes we may mention all those in which heat and chemical affinity play a part. Friction is always accompanied by a decrease and never by an increase of relative velocity; where heat is conducted the warmer body always becomes cooler and the cooler body warmer; in diffusion the process invariably leads to a more thorough mixture and not to a progressive separation of the substances in question. Further, these irreversible events always lead to a definite final state; friction to a relative state of rest, the transfer of heat to temperature equilibrium, and diffusion to a completely homogeneous mixture. On the other hand the former class of reversible events knows neither beginning nor end, so long as no interference takes place from outside, but persists in incessant oscillation.

Now if we wish to introduce unity into the physical view of the universe we must somehow find a formula to cover both these contrasted types of law. How is this indispensable result to be brought about? Some thirty years ago theoretical physics was profoundly influenced by the so-called theory of Energetics, which sought to remove the antithesis by assuming that a fall in temperature, for example, was exactly analogous to the fall of a weight or of a pendulum from a higher to a lower position. This theory, however, did not take into consideration the essential fact that a weight can rise as well as fall, and that a pendulum has reached its greatest velocity at the moment when it has attained its lowest position and therefore, by virtue of its inertia, passes the position of equilibrium and moves to the other side. A transference of heat from a warmer to a colder body, on the contrary, diminishes with the diminution of the difference in temperature, while, of course, there is no such thing as any passing beyond the state of temperature equilibrium by reason of some kind of inertia.

In whatever way we look at it, the contrast between reversible and irreversible processes persists; it must therefore be our task to find some entirely new point of view which will allow us to see that after all there is some connection between the different types of laws. Perhaps we shall succeed in showing that one group of laws is a derivative of the other; if so, the question arises which is to be considered the more simple and elementary—the reversible processes or the irreversible.

Some light is thrown on this question by a formal consideration. Every physical formula contains a number of constant magnitudes, together with variable magnitudes which have to be determined by measurement from case to case. The former magnitudes are fixed once for all and give its characteristic form to the functional connection between the variables which is expressed in the formula. Now if we examine these constants more carefully, we shall find that they invariably are the same for the reversible processes, always recurring, however widely different are the attendant outer conditions. Among these are mass, the gravitation constant, the electrical charge and the velocity of light. On the other hand the constants of the irreversible processes, like the capacity for conducting heat, the coefficient of friction and the diffusion constant, depend to a greater or less degree on external circumstance, e.g. temperature, pressure, etc.

These facts naturally lead us to regard the constants of the first group as the simpler, and the laws dependent on them as the more elementary, and to suppose them incapable of further analysis, while treating the constants of the second group, and the laws depending on them, as being of a somewhat more complex nature. In order to test the validity of this assumption we must make our method of investigation somewhat more exact; we must, so to speak, apply a lens of greater power to the phenomena. If the irreversible processes are in fact composite, then the laws governing them can only be roughly valid, so to say; they must be of a statistical nature, since they are valid only for a large scale view or for summary consideration; that is, for the average values resulting from a large number of distinct processes. The more we restrict the number of individual events on which these average values are based, the more plainly will occasional divergences from the general or macroscopic law make themselves felt. In other words, if in fact the view described is correct, then the laws of the irreversible processes, like those of friction, heat distribution and diffusion, must without exception be inexact if looked at microscopically; they must admit of exceptions in individual cases; and these exceptions will be the more striking, the more careful our examination becomes.

Now it so turned out in the course of events that experience tended more and more to confirm this conclusion. This could come about, of course, only as the result of a great improvement in the methods of making measurements. The laws governing the irreversible processes come so very near to being absolutely valid because of the enormous number of individual events of which these processes are composed. If, for example, we take a liquid having the same uniform temperature throughout, then it follows by the

general or macroscopic law of the conduction of
heat that no heat flows within the liquid. Such
however is not precisely the case. For heat is
the result of slight and rapid movements of the
molecules constituting the liquid; the conduction
of heat, consequently, is due to the transference
of these velocities when the molecules collide.
Hence a uniform temperature does not mean
that all the velocities are equal, but that the
average value of the velocities for each small
quantity of liquid is equal. This quantity in fact
comprises a large number of molecules. But if
we take a quantity containing a relatively small
number of molecules, then the average of their
velocities will vary; and the variation will be
the greater, the smaller is the quantity of liquid.
This principle can nowadays be regarded as a
fact fully proved by experiment. One of the
most striking illustrations is what is known as
the Brownian Movement, which can be observed
through the microscope in small particles of
powder suspended in liquid. These particles are
driven backwards and forwards by the invisible
molecules of the liquid; the movement is the
more pronounced the higher is the temperature.
If we make the further assumption, to which in
principle there is no objection, that each indivi-

dual impulse is a reversible event governed by the strict elementary laws of dynamics, then we may say that the introduction of a microscopic method of examination shows that the laws governing the irreversible processes, or what is the same thing, the laws based upon statistics and mere rough approximation, can be traced back to dynamic, accurate, and absolute laws.

The striking results reached by the introduction of statistical laws in many branches of physical research in recent times have produced a remarkable change in the views of physicists. They no longer, as in the earlier days of Energetics, deny or attempt to cast doubt upon the existence of irreversible processes; instead, the attempt is frequently made to place statistical laws in the foreground, and to subordinate to them laws hitherto regarded as dynamic, including even the law of gravitation. In other words, an attempt is made to exclude absolute law from Nature. And indeed, we cannot but be struck by the fact that the natural phenomena which we can investigate and measure can never be expressed by absolutely accurate numbers; for they inevitably contain a certain inaccuracy introduced by the unavoidable defects of measurement itself. Hence it follows that we shall never succeed in determining by measurement whether a natural law is absolutely valid. If we consider the question from the standpoint of the theory of knowledge we come to the same conclusion. For if we cannot even prove that Nature is governed by law (a difficulty which we meet with at the very outset) *a fortiori* we shall be unable to demonstrate that such law is absolute.

Hence from a logical point of view, we must admit every justification for the hypothesis that the only kind of law in Nature is statistical. It is a different question whether this assumption is expedient in physical research; and I feel strongly inclined to answer this question in the negative. We must consider in the first instance that the only type of law fully satisfying our desire for knowledge is the strictly dynamic type, while every statistical law is fundamentally unsatisfactory, for the simple reason that it has no absolute validity but admits of exceptions in certain cases; so that we are continually faced by the question what these particular exceptional cases are.

Questions of this nature constitute the strongest argument in favour of the extension and further refinement of experimental methods. If it is assumed that statistical laws are the ultimate and most profound type in existence, then there is no reason in theory why, when dealing with any particular statistical law, we should ask what are the causes of the variations in the phenomena? Actually, however, the most important advances in the study of atomic processes are due to the attempt to look for a strictly causal and dynamic law behind every statistical law.

On the other hand, we may discover a law which has always proved absolutely valid within the marginal error due to measurement. In such a case we must admit that it will never be possible to prove by means of measurement that it is not after all of the statistical type. At the same time, it is of great importance whether theoretical considerations induce us to regard the law as being of the statistical, or of the dynamic, type. For in the first case, we should attempt to attain the limits of its validity by means of the continuous refinement of our methods of measurement; in the second case, we should regard such attempts as useless and thus save ourselves much unnecessary labour. So much trouble has already been spent in Physics upon the solution of imaginary problems that such considerations are very far from being irrelevant.

In my opinion, therefore, it is essential for the

healthy development of Physics that among the postulates of this science we reckon, not merely the existence of law in general, but also the strictly causal character of this law. This has in fact almost universally been the case. Further, I consider it necessary to hold that the goal of investigation has not been reached until each instance of a statistical law has been analysed into one or more dynamic laws. I do not deny that the study of statistical laws is of great practical importance: Physics, no less than meteorology, geography and social science, is frequently compelled to make use of statistical laws. At the same time, however, no one will doubt that the alleged accidental variations of the climatological curves, of population statistics and mortality tables, are in each instance subject to strict causality; similarly, physicists will always admit that such questions are strictly relevant as that which asks why one of two neighbouring atoms of Uranium exploded many millions of years before the other.

All studies dealing with the behaviour of the human mind are equally compelled to assume the existence of strict causality. The opponents of this view have frequently brought forward against it the existence of free will. In fact, however, there is no contradiction here; human free will is perfectly compatible with the universal rule of strict causality—a view which I have had occasion to demonstrate in detail elsewhere. But as my arguments on this subject have been seriously misunderstood in certain quarters, and since this subject is surely of considerable importance, I propose to discuss it in some detail here.

§ 7

There has never been any change in the actual position of the problem of free will, and I shall not therefore be in a position to adduce any new facts to this theme. Yet in one respect certain new elements have been added, consisting in the various criticisms, whether positive or negative, which have reached me with regard to the contents and scope of the ideas which I have developed. Naturally these criticisms are of great interest to me, and have been the occasion of certain further considerations. On the present occasion I shall develop these considerations rather further. I do not so much hope to convince my critics of the error of their ways as to contribute to a further elucidation and to a more exact delimitation of the opposing opinions. I may here repeat word for word what I have said on past occasions: that much is implicit in the nature of the case, since after all I am dealing with the same question, a question which probably at one time or another occupies the attention of any thoughtful man. The question is how we can harmonize the consciousness of free will which is alive in us, and which is so closely associated with the sense of responsibility for our actions, with the conviction that every happening is causally determined—which appears to set us free from all responsibility.

The difficulty of finding a satisfactory answer to this question is shown by the fact that there are to-day eminent physicists who think that the law of causality must be sacrificed in order to save free will, and therefore do not hesitate to use the familiar relation of uncertainty of quantum mechanics—which they take as an infraction of the law of causality—in order to explain free will. It is true that they furnish no reply to the question how the assumption of blind chance is to be made compatible with the sense of moral responsibility.

For my part I attempted to show some years ago that it is possible to gain an understanding of the fact of free will and the sense of moral responsibility from the standpoint of natural science, and without any surrender of the assumption of a strict universal rule of causality.

My chief aim in the rest of this book will be to explain this in further detail.

I

To begin our considerations from a fixed starting-point we commence with a point of a scientific nature.

If it is the task of science to look for a law connecting any events in nature or in human life, then it will probably be admitted that the essential condition is that such a law does in fact exist, and can be put in plain language. It is in this sense that I speak of the validity of a general law of causality and of the determination of all the events of the natural and the spiritual world by this law.

Now what do I mean when I say that an event or an action takes place under the necessity of a law, or that it is causally determined? And how do I find out that an event is such a necessity? I can think of no clearer or more convincing demonstration of the necessity of an event than the fact that it is possible to foretell its happening. The question after the origin and nature of causality is here left entirely open: it suffices to state that an event which can be foretold with certainty is in some way causally determined, and conversely that the causal determination of an event implies that the occurrence of the event can be foretold—not of course by anybody, but still by an observer possessing the necessary knowledge of the several circumstances existing at the beginning of the event, and also possessing a sufficient intellectual equipment. Of course such an observer must not interfere in the event. He must make his forecast solely on the strength of the facts known to him and of the conditions which set the event in motion.

I will not here enter on the difficult question whether there can ever in practice be so intelligent and so passive an observer, and how, if such there be, he acquires the necessary information. Such a question would lead us to a special investigation of the sense and validity of the law of causality, and this is not essential to the treatment of the present theme. At this point it suffices to be sure that the imaginary introduction of an observer of the kind described leads to no logical or empirical contradiction.

II

We will assume, in conformity with what has been said, that there is a fixed causal connection in all the events of nature and of the spiritual world; and further, in what follows, I shall confine myself to human acts of will. It is clear that it would be nonsense to speak of a universal causality if there were any exception to it; if, in other words, the events of the soul's conscious and subconscious life, the feelings, sensations, thoughts, and also the will, were not subject to the law of causality as determined above. We therefore assume that the human will, too, is causally determined; that is, that in every instance where a man manifests will in a definite way, either quite readily or as the result of long deliberation, or again where he has to make a definite decision, an observer if sufficiently intelligent, and if he remained perfectly passive would be in a position to foretell the behaviour of the man in question. We may imagine this in this way that before the eye of the apprehending observer the will of the man whom he observes comes about as the result of the joint action of a number of motives or impulses which act within him with different force and in different directions

—whether with or without his knowledge—and which result within him in a certain event, much in the same way as that in which in physics different forces compose themselves into one resultant force. It is true that the interplay of the various motives acting in many different directions is infinitely more subtle and complicated than that of the natural forces; and it is an enormous demand on the intelligence of the observer to ask that he shall be able to recognize the causal conditions of the several motives and properly to appreciate their significance. We must even admit that among men actually alive such a delicate observer will certainly not be found. However, it has already been expressly stated that we will not touch on this difficulty since it suffices that there can be no logical objection to the assumption that there is an observer endowed with any degree of intelligence which it may please us to assign to him.

It is to be noted, in fact, that this assumption is the foundation and the starting-point of any scientific investigation whether in the sphere of history or of psychology. The historian tries to interpret every historical event and every manifestation of the will of historical persons as determined by law—by their personality and by the circumstances; and if there are any gaps he does not put these down to a suspension of the principle of causality, i.e. to chance, but to his own lack of knowledge of the actual facts. The psychologist similarly in all his experiments and investigations assumes as far as possible the standpoint of an omniscient observer who is compelled, however, to remain entirely passive. Any influence exerted on the train of the observed person's thought—even if unintentional—would disturb the causal nexus which it is desired to study, and would introduce error into the conclusions drawn. Even the fact that the object of the experiment is aware that he is under observation can, of course, become a dangerous source of error.

In practical life as well as in science we are continually assuming the validity of a strictly causal determinism. In our dealings with our fellow-humans we always arrange our actions in such a manner that a given manifestation on our part shall have a given influence upon their will. The better we know a man, the more surely can we judge his presumable behaviour, and if his behaviour disappoints our expectations we do not infer that the causal nexus has been suspended, but that circumstances unknown to us or insufficiently observed have been at work. Even behaviour which we describe as caprice or whim is assigned not to accident, but to a certain characteristic disposition of the person in question. In no case can we make any progress without assuming that the principle of causality is uninterrupted.

III

It will aid our further considerations if we take a definite example. Let us assume, therefore, that an innocent person, who is being pursued, has been secretly brought to a hidden place by a courageous friend, and that the friend is visited by the pursuers, who ask him where the man is hidden. What will his behaviour be? If he is a man of high ethical principles there will be a conflict between his love of the truth and his loyalty to a friend. A truthful answer to the question would mean certain destruction for his friend; and thus it might occur to him, in order to stick to the truth, to refuse an answer, and further to do all that lay in his power to establish the innocence of the fugitive. But in that case the only result might be that forcible methods would be applied to him in order to compel him to speak out. It would be far simpler, and would hold a better hope for the fugitive's safety, if he were to set the pursuers on the false track by a lie: and were to indicate, not the real hiding-place, but a distant locality. In this way he would at any rate gain time. But there are also other lines of conduct. He might reply that he did not know the hiding-place, or he might procrastinate, or he might not reply at all, and pretend to be deaf. Each line of conduct has its advantages and its disadvantages; with the result that in the questioned man's mind a great number of considerations might be in conflict, each of which contributes to the motives determining his resolution, and all of which he must weigh against each other. Nor are these considerations the only motives leading to his decision. There is a legion of motives and impulses which are but dimly conscious to the man, if at all. These are moods, impulses, and perhaps also inhibitions flowing from his character and temperament—intensified possibly by excitement—about which he does not clearly account to himself, though they may well play a very important part in the conflict of motives.

But however manifold and complex this play of forces may be, nevertheless before the eye of

the observer whom we have assumed to comprehend all this the interplay of the totality of the
motives—here and subsequently I use motive
for convenience' sake in a rather wider than the
usual sense—there comes about a perfectly
definite result which he is able to foresee: and the
decision of the man whom he is observing will
conform exactly with this result. Such is the
postulate of the general law of causality.

Now what is the position if the observer communicates in all its details the result to the man
who is in the process of deliberating, immediately
before he reaches the conclusion of his deliberations? Will the latter in that case invariably
decide in the sense of the information he has just
received? It would be rash to make such a claim.
For now the observer has ceased to be passive,
and is interfering in the causal train of the event
which he had been observing. Indeed, the observed
person is now faced with a new situation. For
one thing he will have heard something new
about the motives which had been guiding him
in the course of his deliberations. For example,
he will learn whether the decision which he would
have reached if he had not been told anything
by the observer would have been chiefly influenced by conscious or by subconscious motives:

and on the strength of this new information he will be able to check and possibly to alter his original decision. In this case similar considerations will be at work as before, with the difference that there will now also be at work new motives emerging from the fresh information he had received. Nor can there be any doubt that on the present occasion again the observer will be able fully to comprehend the causal nexus, and that, since he has a complete knowledge of the person under observation and of the circumstances, he will be able to foretell exactly how he will react to the information he has received. However, he will only then react with certainty in the manner foreseen if he is not once again told about it by the observer; since otherwise a new situation arises for him, and the whole process continues *ad infinitum*. It will never be possible to claim with certainty that the observed person's decision will remain uninfluenced by some new and immediately preceding information; and the observer will always be able to foretell his behaviour. For on the one hand the observed person, although the observer should completely comprehend his motives, need in no circumstances obey the latter; and on the other hand it lies entirely with him to change or not to change the direction of his will in conformity with the information which he has received. On the other hand, the observer in each case recognizes the causal determination of the behaviour of the observed person, and is able to foretell whether the latter, whether from caprice or from a certain spirit of contradiction, will or will not oppose himself to the communication made to him. The essential point is that at each new communication the observed person is presented with a new fact, and that this fact causes him to revise his deliberations at the stage which they have actually reached. In this process fresh motives may arise. We are led to the conclusion that nobody, however much information he may receive, can become so clever that nothing he may be told can possibly be news to him—a conclusion to which the profoundest thinkers will probably have least to object.

IV

In order to approach nearer to our main problem we will now do justice to actual facts, and substitute for the ideal and absolutely percipient observer a person standing in the midst of every-day life; and we will ask to what extent such a man is able to understand the causal determination of human acts of will. This change implies two important differences from the assumptions we have made so far. First, however intelligent such an observer may be, it is out of the question that he should apprehend completely the motives of the observed person. He cannot therefore foretell exactly his decisions: at best he may expect a certain action with a greater or less degree of justification. The greater the intellectual superiority of the observer over the observed person, the more certain will his forecast be. Here there is obviously no limit which can be indicated with exactitude; but in principle there is no reason why the observer's intelligence should not be taken as being so great, relatively to that of the observed person, as to give to his forecast any desired degree of accuracy.

There is also a second difference. In actual life an observer frequently is unable to remain perfectly passive; and we saw that a passive attitude was an essential condition for the recognition of the causal trains at work in an event which is under observation. In many instances certain tests are necessary to afford information about the case in question, and such tests often interfere with the events which it is desired to investigate. Thus extreme caution is here requisite from the very beginning, and we shall see that in the most important case of all we find at this point a limit imposed not by the facts, but by the nature of the case.

We now pass to the most important phase of all, just mentioned. It is the observation of our own will-actions. To what extent are we able to comprehend the causal determination of our own will? Evidently the only possibility is to attempt a division of our ego into a percipient and a willing ego, to the first of which we assign the part of observer, while to the second we give that of observed. In this case there is an important difference if the will-action belongs to the past and if it belongs to the present. If the action has already taken place the desired condition is fulfilled that the observer shall be passive; for in this case the willing ego chronologically precedes and the percipient ego comes later, and there can be no causal interference by the observer in the event which he is investigating. The fact is that all our past will-actions, like all other past events, lie perfect and finished before our inner eye, and we are in a position to regard them as unchangeable objects. It depends on the greater or less development of our knowledge and our judgment whether and how we reach a later understanding of their causal determination—i.e. their arising out of conscious or subconscious motives. There is a wide difference between our actual capacity for understanding and that of the ideal observer whom we were assuming before; but this difference is of a merely practical and not of a fundamental nature. And to this extent we may say that a complete understanding of the causal course of our own past will-actions, down to the most obscure motives, is entirely within the realm of theoretical possibility.

But the case is altered when our action lies in the future, for then the observer ceases to be passive. The observed and the observer, the willing and the percipient ego, are merged in our consciousness, and it is impossible for the observer to avoid any causal interference with the observed. It is a dangerous self-deception for us to assume that we can play the part of a disinterested observer watching our future actions from on high, and that we can restrict ourselves to pure contemplation. It is, of course, possible to turn on our late and early actions the scrutiny of pure understanding, and to this extent the fictitious division of the ego into a willing and acting, and

into a percipient part, can in fact be carried
through to a certain extent; but at the moment
where we consciously make a decision the one
ego merges with the other, and thus at this one
moment their separation, even in the merely
theoretical sense, is a logical impossibility—a
contradictio in adjecto. The consequences as far
as our problem is concerned are most clearly
apparent if we undertake a mental self-obser-
vation, and if, assuming the strict validity of the
principle of causality, we attempt to find out how
a future will-action comes about, advancing our
investigation step by step.

This is the question: Can we, at least in theory,
understand our own motives so exactly and so
completely that we are able to foretell accurately
the decisions necessarily arising from their
interplay? Let us imagine ourselves in the position of the man whom we were considering in our
former example; the man who was deliberating
his behaviour in a given difficult position. Like
this man, we will consider all the possibilities and
weigh their several advantages and disadvantages,
and will try thence to derive the direction and
strength of the resulting motives. In doing so we
shall be acting like an observer who, standing
outside, sees through the events taking place in

the mind of the observed person and records the origin of the various conflicting motives. But in the present case the observer is far from remaining passive; on the contrary he immediately communicates the result of each observation he makes to the observed person, with the result that a condition arises resembling that described in connection with the former case. Each new observation—as was explained in detail—gives rise to a new motive, and the recognition of this motive in turn creates a new situation. The series is infinite, and since the observed person (the willing ego) owes no obedience to the observer (the percipient ego), we shall never be able to claim with certainty that the eventual decision must be in the sense of the observer's latest discovery. On the contrary, subconscious motives will always play their part here. Self-knowledge has, in practice, a limit. And thus, while in theory at least a causal understanding of a man's past action is possible, a complete understanding of a man's present motives, and hence a causal understanding of his future, always remains unattainable.

Accordingly all those who make such an understanding the criterion of free will are, in my opinion, involved in a fundamental error.

Nor would a closer approach to free will be effected if we were to claim that the attainment of such an understanding is a goal which, though infinitely distant in practice, is attainable in theory. For the fact is that free will is not infinitely distant: it is immediately present to each one of us, and it is vouched for by the sense of moral responsibility which is so closely connected with it, and which weighs on us in every hour of our daily actions. Indeed, it seems to me that it stands in inverse ratio with the understanding we possess of our motives. The more detailed is the insight which we obtain into the causal determination of our motives, the more the sense of responsibility vanishes which we feel for the consequences of the decision which we may reach; and a complete insight into our motives would—in my opinion—entirely banish free will. A man completely understanding the strength and direction of all his motives would be saved the trouble of further deliberation, and would feel that his eventual decision was inevitable. But things can never reach this stage. A man in the process of his deliberation may weigh the motives of an impending action with any degree of care and completeness, yet nothing prevents him from breaking through the chain of the conclusions he is drawing, and from suddenly doing the very opposite of the action which a long course of deliberation had just led him to approve. We all have made this observation in ourselves: it is an observation which destroys every theory to the contrary.

It might then seem as though our free will rested on a gap in our capacity for understanding. Such a formulation, however, would be wholly erroneous. It is an intellectual impossibility completely to understand the events in our own subconscious; but nobody would set this down to a deficiency in our faculty for understanding, any more than one would put down to a runner's slowness the fact that he can never overtake himself, however much he may increase his speed. The fact is that free will rests neither on the inadequacy of our understanding nor upon a complete insight into our motives. Nor does it rest, as is so frequently asserted to-day, on a gap in the causal nexus. What it does rest upon is the fact that a man's will is prior to his understanding, or in other words that his character is more important than his intellect. The understanding may influence, but can never dominate the will. However far the understanding may lead us to penetrate into the obscurity of our own motives, it is the will which is sovereign in the final decision, and it decides without consulting the understanding. The best illustration of which I can think of the profound truth of this claim is the reply given by a lady—it is true that this happened a number of years ago—when she had been given an exhaustive scientific explanation: "Yes, I quite understand all this. But I still don't believe it."

But at the same time our will, like our character, remains strictly subjected to causality. Only, in order that the law of causality shall have a meaning, we must assume that the observer is able completely to apprehend our entire physical and mental condition—the conscious as well as the subconscious. The dull or the arrogant claim that such an observer is unthinkable proves only that the person who makes it is lacking either in imagination or in reverence; and the latter is an essential condition for any fruitful occupation with the deepest questions of ethics and epistemology.

V

It results from our investigation that the opposition between a strict causality and free will is merely apparent, and that the difficulty lies in an appropriate formulation of the problem. The question whether the will is or is not subject to causality is answered differently in accordance with the standpoint taken up for our consideration. Looked at objectively, from the outside, the will is subject to causality; looked at from the inside, or subjectively, it is free. In other words, another person's will is subject to causality, and all his will-actions can be understood and foretold in all their details—at least in theory—as the necessary consequence of the law of causality, provided that all the precedent conditions are sufficiently well known. The degree to which this can be done in practice depends on the observer's intelligence. A man's own will, on the other hand, can be causally understood only as far as his past actions are concerned, and it is impossible for his future actions to be inferred by a process of pure understanding from his present state and from the influence of his environment, however highly his intelligence may be trained.

There is an obvious objection to this formulation which I wish to examine more closely at this point. It has been urged that we began by taking the law of causality as the condition of any scientific investigation, and that it applies strictly

to all will-actions, but that, this having been done,
indeterminism is admitted by the back entrance
and is allowed a certain weight. This, it is alleged,
is contradictory, or at any rate obscure, since the
will is either subject to determination or not,
there being no third way.

This objection is based on an inadmissible
confusion of two distinct points of view: in order
to refute it I should like to bring forward a simple
example from physics. We know that any quantitative predication about a spatial-temporal event
has a definite meaning only if the system of
reference is indicated for which it is supposed to
be valid. This system can be selected at pleasure,
and in accordance with the different systems
chosen the predication too will differ. Thus if a
system of reference closely connected with the
earth is taken we must say that the sun moves
through the heavens, but if the system of reference is transposed to a star the sun is at rest.
There is an opposition between these two formulations, but there is neither contradiction nor
obscurity: we are simply dealing with two
different ways of looking at the matter. According
to the physical theory of relativity—which
to-day can surely be counted among the definite
acquisitions of science—the two systems of

reference and the two corresponding points of view are equally correct and equally justified, and it is in principle impossible to employ any measurements or calculations, in order to chose between them, save in an arbitrary manner.

If we now revert to the matter in hand we find that here, too, there are two points of view of equal validity, and that we must make a free choice between them before we can make any definite predication about free will. The objective point of view which science must employ corresponds to the standpoint of the completely passive observer. Here the law of causality is of universal validity, and the human will, like every other happening, is strictly determined: and this is true even of the most subtle events in the world of the spirit. True, to understand the causality of creative works of genius an intelligence of an incredibly high and even divine order is requisite: but in principle I can see no objection to such an assumption. Before the eyes of God even the loftiest human intellects are like rudimentary structures. Yet this does not detract from the mysterious aura which surrounds these rare intellects, nor from the lofty height in which they are situated to our eyes.

However, the standpoint of objective science

or of the highest intelligence is not the only valid one, nor the most obvious. Nor is it even the primitive standpoint; it is one which must be achieved with a greater or less degree of toil. On the other hand, the subjective-personal standpoint is one which has an equal validity and a more immediate obviousness; though it is true that it is different for different people, and hence unsuitable for scientific considerations. Seen from this—i.e. from the individual point of view, a man's own will cannot be determined and is therefore free. This assertion no more contradicts the fact that the will is objectively determined than the fact that the sun is in motion subjectively contradicts its objective state of rest. When we are observing ourselves what matters is not that we *are*, but that we *feel* ourselves to be free. This kind of freedom may be described as an illusion; but in that case every feeling is illusory. For the feelings can never be nailed down in an objectively scientific manner; they can only be experienced personally, and if they are so experienced they are simple immediate data and their effect is independent of our judgment about them.

The controversy about the freedom of will thus is revealed as a controversy about the point of view. In my opinion there is not here a problem present capable of a definitive solution, nor do I think that the case will be altered so long as men think and act.

VI

We have thus been led to the discovery that the causal point of view fails us precisely at the point which is of the chief importance for the conduct of life. Neither science nor self-knowledge can give us a full light on our future action in any given situation; a different guide is needed for this end, a guide acting not on the understanding but, immediately, on the will, by providing us with rules of conduct for given situations. It follows that science requires a complement for the gap it has left. This complement is ethics, which adds to the causal "must" the moral "shall," and places by the side of pure cognition the judgment of value which is strange to the causal scientific point of view.

A satisfactory formulation of ethics is perhaps the chief and the hardest problem of the human spirit. The profoundest thinkers have exercised themselves upon it since the beginnings of civilization. It is not a subject to which I venture to offer a contribution: I am not a teacher of ethics, nor do I feel any call in that direction. I desire, however, in this connection, to say a few words about the predications which it is possible to make about ethics, its meaning and content, from the scientific point of view. It is true that ethics is not based on science; but on the other hand it cannot wholly detach itself from science, and must certainly not enter into conflict with it. Thus ethics has, and also has not, much in common with science.

There is one science only, common to all civilized peoples, though it is also true that every science grows on a national soil. On the other hand, many different ethical systems have been worked out in the course of centuries; and between these there has often been acute conflict. Different ethical theories are even found to be in conflict within a civilization which, geographically and chronologically, is one. I need here recall only the difference between civil and political morals. It is easier to distinguish between true and false than between valuable and valueless.

Now what is the criterion of the value of a system of ethics? In my opinion there can be one reply only. That system of ethics is best which proves itself to be the best in practical life; just as in science that theory should be preferred which best fits experience. Deeply aware of this truth, the greatest teachers of ethics have always felt it to be their chief task to promote the practical application of their teaching, in which enterprise they set an example themselves; while the greatest among them, from Socrates to Jesus, did not hesitate to give their lives for this cause. We may even say that this upright championship of their teaching is an essential characteristic of their greatness.

A glance at the present reveals a different picture. Compared with those great men the modern moralists look poor and petty who erect a pretentious edifice, with all the arts of logic and dialectics available to them, but who apparently have no thought of applying to themselves their own ethical postulates, and disdainfully reject any suggestion in this sense as though it were a most improper imputation. These clever professors seem to have no suspicion that such an attitude blocks the only road which might lead their system to a more general recognition. What would we say of a physicist or a chemist who should work out an ambitious and a mathematically faultless theory, but who should deny the justification or admissibility of any attempt to apply it to the events of nature? A system of such a kind would not be taken seriously; it would be passed over in favour of more important matters. In ethics, on the other hand, less exacting claims are made: in this sphere at any rate authors of some reputation are found who do not dream of applying their own rules—which nevertheless claim universal validity—to their own actions.

This is particularly true of those moralists who deny the value of life. It is true that the suffering and injustice of life justifies the question whether the sum of evil and sorrow in the world outweighs the sum of the good and the pleasant; and indeed it would appear to be one of the hardest tasks of ethics to provide, in the sad confusion of the contemporary civilized world, in the deplorable conflict of interests and opinions, and in the hopeless disharmony which we find in so many places the guiding lines which will give us a fixed hold—that is, something that shall furnish us with a lasting concord with our own self in the conduct of life: with an inner peace. This difficulty, as such, is removed in the simplest way if the value of life is denied and the struggle for its preservation and enrichment is hence declared to be meaningless. But in such a case it must not be forgotten that any ethics proceeding from such a foundation can be justified only by the demonstration that a practically useful guide for actual life can thence be derived. And no doubt this is what the ancient Indian sages felt when, convinced of the vanity of earthly goods, they withdrew altogether from the outer world, and tried as far as possible to render themselves independent of the needs of life by the practice of a profound self-absorption.

Striking indeed is the contrast between these men and those modern moralists who, while making the negation of life the programme of their world-view, are busy and active practitioners of the art of *savoir vivre*. It is an obvious question to ask what are the ethical rules which in practice guide these versatile people when they come to act, but it is a question to which no answer is vouchsafed. How to explain this strange contradiction? Can it be that these exponents do not really take their own teaching seriously and see in it no more than an amusing and interesting intellectual game? No graver charge could be made against any philosopher, and I think that there is a more obvious explanation, and one which at any rate does not touch the honesty of these people. My assumption is that the motives derived from their own ethics of life-negation are balanced, and indeed overcome by more vigorous and opposite motives derived from the natural impulses towards self-preservation and self-assertion which sleep in the subconscious: yet another proof of the general truth that the human will, which emerges from the obscure depths, is stronger than the consciously deliberating understanding. We saw that this proposition was the basis of a man's own free will: the practical actions of our life are dictated, not by scientific knowledge based on rational consideration, but by the free will which directs itself towards ethical ends.

Thus each man carries his fate freely in his hand. We cannot, attentive but neutral watchers, observe the way in which a law controls the course of our own vital struggles; we are ourselves actively involved in the battle and hence are compelled to take one side or the other in accordance with our free choice. No fatalism can relieve us of responsibility.

It would be a dangerous deception if we were to adopt a fatalistic passivity and idly to wait for what was going to happen in the belief that time spent on thinking about our future actions could only be wasted since they were predetermined by the law of causality. In fact this decision itself would be a free decision of the will. The best and the most natural safeguard against such moral aberrations is provided by the voice of conscience. And even where the bias of disposition or an exaggerated concentration on immature social theories has warped the judgment and removed natural inhibitions, there ought at any rate to be an awareness, reached as a matter of understanding, that the law of causality which, as we saw, is meaningless when applied to our momentary mental state—cannot possibly be invoked in order to relieve us of responsibility for our immediately impending actions. On the other hand, the fact that we can never have a full causal understanding of our future actions gives us the right to allow full play to our imagination and opens the door even to the boldest optimism.

It is only when an action has been completed and belongs to the past that we are justified in attempting to understand it from the purely causal point of view. To recognize that definite though at the moment inapprehensible causal laws extend to our ethical actions is not only important as a matter of scientific knowledge, but can also be of value on practical life—especially when we regret an action because of its intended or unintended consequences. By looking into the causal nexus we are often enabled to acquire the necessary insight which shall allow us in a future case of the kind to avoid the past errors and commit no new ones.

It is true that a late analysis of the causes of faulty action does not make good the harm done nor remove dissatisfaction; and indeed it is in some respects dangerous to indulge in an over-anxious consideration of events which, though regrettable, are over and done with. On the other hand we may experience a sensible relief and a lifting of our depression if we realize even after the event that in the circumstances and the mental disposition of the time the only possible motives which could have decided us were those which in fact did determine our action. Though the regrettable consequences are not altered, we can contemplate the course of events more calmly and can spare ourselves the bitter and lasting remorse with which some people in such a case plague themselves for the rest of their lives.

But this is not all. If, on looking back on what we regard as an unpleasant event, we honestly try to understand all the consequences, we may well be led to discover that something which we at one time regarded as a misfortune has worked out as a benefit—for example, because, though a sacrifice, it led to a higher advantage, or because it saved us from a greater misfortune. In such a case our regret may be changed into satisfaction and pleasure. In this connection a profound meaning attaches to the popular saying: "Who knows to what good it may lead?" We never can tell whether such satisfactory consequences may not reveal themselves in the future; and in principle there is no reason for not assuming that they arise sooner or later in every case, though we may not always possess the necessary insight to observe them. We may congratulate those who succeed in raising themselves to this view of life, which can be refuted neither by science nor by logic, and which, as we saw, is the product of the will and not of the understanding. Such people will always be ready to accept the goodness and beauty of the moment, while carrying a charm against the inner and outer dangers which permanently threaten the harmony of the soul.

So far I have necessarily restricted myself to a consideration of the law of causality in relation to the individual. Free will, like the sense of responsibility, has a meaning ultimately only with reference to the individual. However, it is certain that there is a communal or popular will as well as an individual will. The former is something more than the sum of the individual wills. Further, it is certain that this kind of will, whose spatial and temporal validity is much greater, is subject to similar laws. I should accordingly like to end by summing up the conclusions which we can reach immediately from what has preceded. A people's history is causally intelligible only so far as the past is concerned, and its future can never be established on purely scientific lines. Any attempt to solve the question whether it is in the ascendant or in a decline by purely historical methods is doomed to failure, a fact which is happily being more and more widely recognized. At the same time we can confidently say that the future will belong to that race and that people which calls up, and manifests, the necessary will.

§ 8

Let us, however, return to Physics, from which these complications are excluded in advance. I propose now to describe the more important characteristics of the current view of the physical world. These characteristics are due to the endeavour to find a strict causal connection, in the manner described above, for all physical processes. A cursory glance suffices to show what changes there have been since the beginning of the century; and we may say that since the days of Galileo and Newton, no such rapid development has ever been known. Incidentally we may point with pride to the fact that German scientists have played an important part in this advance. The occasion of this development was that extreme refinement in measurement which is an essential condition of the progress of science and engineering; in its turn this led to the discovery of new facts, and hence to the revision and improvement of theory. Two new ideas in particular have given modern Physics its characteristic shape. These are laid down in the Theory of Relativity and the Quantum hypothesis respectively; each in its own way is at once fruitful and revolutionary; but they have nothing in common and, in a sense, they are even antagonistic.

For a time Relativity was a universal topic of conversation. The arguments for and against could be heard everywhere—even in the daily Press, where it was championed and opposed by experts and by others who were very far from being experts. To-day things have quieted down a little—a state of affairs which is likely to please nobody better than the author of the Theory himself; public interest appears to have become satisfied and to have turned to other popular topics. From this it might perhaps be inferred that the Theory of Relativity no longer plays any part in science. But as far as I can judge, the opposite is the case, for the Theory of Relativity has now become part and parcel of the physical view of the world, and is taken for granted without any further ado. Indeed, novel and revolutionary as was the idea of Relativity (in both the Special and the General form) when first presented to physicists, the fact remains that the assertions it makes and the attacks it delivers were directed not against the outstanding, recognized and approved laws of Physics, but only against certain views which had no better sanction than custom, deeply rooted though they were. These standpoints are of the kind which, as I have already tried to show, afford a suitable basis for a preliminary understanding of the facts of Physics; but they must be discarded as soon as it is found necessary to reach a more general and profound view of the facts.

In this connection the idea of simultaneity is particularly instructive. At first glance, it seems to the observer that nothing could be more obviously true than to say that there is a definite meaning in asserting that two events occurring at two distant points (e.g. on the Earth and on Mars) are simultaneous. Surely every man has a right to traverse great distances timelessly in thought, and to place two events side by side before the mind's eye. Now it must be emphasized that the Theory of Relativity does not alter this right in any way. If we possess sufficiently accurate measuring instruments, we can determine with complete certainty whether the events are simultaneous; and if the time measurements are accurately made in different ways, and with different instruments which can be used to check each other, the same result will always be obtained. To this extent the Theory of Relativity has brought about no change whatever.

But the Theory of Relativity does not allow us to assume, as a matter of course, that another observer who is moving relatively to ourselves must necessarily regard the two events as simultaneous. For the thoughts and ideas of one person are not necessarily the thoughts and ideas of another. If the two observers proceed to discuss their thoughts and ideas, each will appeal to his own measurements; and when they do this, it will be found that in interpreting their respective measurements they started from entirely different assumptions. Which assumption is correct it is impossible to decide; and it is equally impossible to decide the dispute as to which of the two observers is in a state of rest, and which in a state of motion. This question, however, is of fundamental importance, for the rate of a clock alters while the clock is being moved—a fact which need occasion no surprise; while from this it follows that the clocks of the two observers go at different rates. Thus we reach the conclusion that each can assert with an equal right that he is himself in a state of rest and that his time measurements are correct; and this in spite of the fact that the one observer regards the two events as simultaneous, while the other does not. These ideas and arguments admittedly present a hard task to our powers of imagination; but the sacrifice in clarity is negligible compared with the inestimable advantages which follow from the amazing generality and simplicity of the physical world-view which they render possible.

In spite of this, some readers may still find themselves unable to get rid of the suspicion that the Theory of Relativity contains some kind of internal contradiction. Such readers should reflect that a theory, the entire content of which can be expressed in a single mathematical formula, can no more contain a contradiction than could two distinct conclusions following from the same formula. Our ideas must adjust themselves to the results of the formula and not conversely. Ultimately it is experience that must decide the admissibility and the importance of the Theory of Relativity. Indeed, the fact that experience allows us to test its validity must be looked upon as the most important evidence in favour of the fruitfulness of the theory. Hitherto no instance has been recorded where the Theory conflicts with experience, a fact which I should like to emphasize in view of certain reports which have recently come before the public. Anyone who, for whatever reason, considers it possible or probable that a conflict between the Theory and observed facts can be discovered, could do no better than co-operate in extending the Theory of Relativity and in pushing its conclusions as far as possible, since this is the only means of refuting it through experience. Such an undertaking is the less difficult because the assertions made by the Theory of Relativity are simple and comparatively easy to apprehend, so that they fit into the framework of classical Physics without any difficulty.

Indeed, if there were no historical objections I

personally would not hesitate for a moment to
include the Theory of Relativity within the body
of classical Physics. In a manner the Theory of
Relativity is the crowning point of Physics, since
by merging the ideas of Time and Space it has
also succeeded in uniting under a higher point
of view such concepts as those of mass, energy,
gravitation, and inertia. As the result of this
novel view we have the perfectly symmetrical
form which the laws of the conservation of energy
and of momentum now assume; for these laws
follow with equal validity from the Principle of
Least Action—that most comprehensive of all
physical laws which governs equally mechanics
and electrodynamics.

Now over against this strikingly imposing and
harmonious structure there stands the Quantum
Theory, an extraneous and threatening explosive
body which has already succeeded in producing
a wide and deep fissure throughout the whole of
the structure. Unlike the Theory of Relativity,
the Quantum Theory is not complete in itself.
It is not a single, harmonious, and perfectly
transparent idea, modifying the traditional facts
and concepts of Physics by means of a change
which, though of the utmost significance in theory,
is practically hardly noticeable. On the contrary,

it first arose as a means of escape from an *impasse* reached by classical Physics in one particular branch of its studies—the explanation of the laws of radiant heat. It was soon seen, however, that it also solved with ease, or at least considerably helped to elucidate, other problems which were causing unmistakable difficulties to the classical theory, such as photoelectric phenomena, specific heat, ionization, and chemical reactions. Thus it was quickly realized that the Quantum Theory must be regarded, not merely as a working hypothesis, but as a new and fundamental principle of Physics, whose significance becomes evident wherever we are dealing with rapid and subtle phenomena.

Now here we are faced with a difficulty. This does not so much consist in the fact that the Quantum Theory contradicts the traditional views; if that were all, it follows from what has been said that the difficulty need not be taken very seriously. It arises from the fact that in the course of time it has become increasingly obvious that the Quantum Theory unequivocally denies certain fundamental views which are essential to the whole structure of the classical theory. Hence the introduction of the Quantum Theory is not a modification of the classical theory, as is the case with the Theory of Relativity: it is a complete break with the classical theory.

Now if the Quantum Theory were superior or equal to the classical theory at all points, it would be not only feasible but necessary to abandon the latter in favour of the former. This, however, is definitely not the case. For there are parts of Physics, among them the wide region of the phenomena of interference, where the classical theory has proved its validity in every detail, even when subjected to the most delicate measurements; while the Quantum Theory, at least in its present form, is in these respects completely useless. It is not the case that the Quantum Theory cannot be applied, but that, when applied, the results reached do not agree with experience.

The result of this state of affairs is that at the present moment each theory has what may be called its own preserve, where it is safe from attack, while there is also an intermediate region —e.g. that of the phenomena of the dispersion and scattering of light—where the two theories compete with varying fortunes. The two theories are approximately of equal usefulness, so that physicists are guided in the choice of theory by their private predilections—an uncomfortable

and, in the long run, an intolerable state of
affairs for anyone desirous of reaching the true
facts.

To illustrate this curious condition of things
I will select a particular example from a very
large number collected by workers in the field
of theory and of practice. I begin by stating
two facts. Let us imagine two fine pencils of
rays of violet light, produced by placing an
opaque screen with two small holes over against
the light which is given out from a point source.
The two pencils of rays emerging from the holes
can be reflected so that they meet on the surface
of a white wall at some distance away. In this
case the spot of light which they jointly pro-
duce on the wall is not uniformly bright, but is
traversed by dark lines. This is the first fact.
The second is this—if any metal that is sensitive
to light is placed in the path of one of these rays,
the metal will continually emit electrons with a
velocity independent of the intensity of the light.

Now if the intensity of the source of light is
allowed to decrease, then in the first case, according to all the results hitherto obtained, the dark
lines remain quite unchanged; it is only the
strength of the illumination that decreases. In
the other case, however, the velocity of the elec-

trons emitted also remains quite unchanged, and the only change that takes place is that the emission becomes less copious.

Now how do the theories account for these two facts? The first is adequately explained by the classical theory as follows: at every point of the white wall which is simultaneously illuminated by the two pencils of rays, the two rays which meet at this point either strengthen or else weaken each other, according to the relations between their respective wave-lengths. The second fact is equally satisfactorily explained by the Quantum Theory, which maintains that the energy of the rays falls on the sensitive metal, not in a continuous flow, but in an intermittent succession of more or less numerous, equal and indivisible quanta, and that each quantum, as it impinges on the metal, detaches one electron from the mass. On the other hand, all attempts have failed hitherto to explain the lines of interference by the Quantum Theory and the photoelectric effect by the classical theory. For if the energy radiated really travels only in indivisible quanta, then a quantum emitted from the source of light can pass only through one or else the other of the two holes in the opaque screen; while if the light is sufficiently feeble, it is also impossible for two distinct rays to impinge simultaneously on a single point on the white wall; hence interference becomes impossible. In fact the lines invariably disappear completely, as soon as one of the rays is cut off.

On the other hand, if the energy radiated from a point-source of light spreads out uniformly through space, its intensity must necessarily be diminished. Now it is not easy to see how the velocity with which an electron is emitted from the sensitive metal can be equally great whether it is subjected to very powerful or to very weak radiation. Naturally many attempts have been made to get over this difficulty. Perhaps the most obvious way was to assume that the energy of the electron emitted by the metal is not derived from the radiation falling on it, but that it comes from the interior of the metal, so that the effect of the radiation is merely to set it free in the same way as a spark sets free the latent energy of gunpowder. It has, however, not proved possible to demonstrate that there is such a source of energy, or even to make it appear plausible that there should be such a source. Another supposition is that, while the energy of the electrons is derived from the radiation impinging upon them, the electrons themselves are not actually emitted from the metal until this has been subjected to the illumination for a time sufficiently long to allow the energy necessary for a definite velocity to have been accumulated. This process, however, might take minutes or even hours, whereas in fact the phenomenon repeatedly takes place very much sooner. Light is thrown on the profound importance of these difficulties by the fact that in highly influential quarters the suggestion has arisen of sacrificing the validity of the principle of the conservation of energy. This may well be described as a desperate remedy; in this particular instance, in fact, it was soon proved to be untenable by means of experiments.

Hitherto, then, all attempts to understand the laws of the emission of electrons from the standpoint of the classical theory have failed. On the other hand these, and a number of other laws relating to the reciprocal action of radiation and matter, become immediately intelligible and even necessary as soon as we assume that light quanta travel through space in the shape of minute, individual structures and that, when impinging upon matter, they behave like really substantial atoms.

We are compelled, however, to decide in favour

of one or the other view; so that the whole problem obviously resolves itself into the question whether the radiant energy emitted from the source of light is divided when it leaves this source, so that one part of it passes through one of the holes in the opaque screen and the remainder through the other, or whether the energy passes in indivisible quanta alternately through each of the two holes. Every theory of quanta must answer this question, and must deal with it in some manner or other; hitherto, however, no physicist has succeeded in giving a satisfactory answer.

It has sometimes been suggested that the difficulties of the Quantum Theory do not so much apply to the propagation of radiation in free space as to the reciprocal action which takes place between radiation and matter carrying an electric charge. With this opinion I cannot agree. The question set out above confines itself to the propagation of radiation, and there is no reference either to its causes or to its effects.

It might indeed be asked whether we have a right to speak of the energy of free radiation as though it were something actual, since the fact is that all measurements invariably relate to events taking place in material bodies. If we wish to maintain the absolute validity of the energy principle, a standpoint which recent investigation renders particularly plausible, then there can be no doubt that we must assign to every field of radiation a quite definite, and more or less exactly calculable, amount of energy, which is decreased by the absorption of radiation and increased by its emission. The question now is, what is the behaviour of this energy? Once this question is asked, it becomes plain beyond the possibility of doubt that we must make up our minds to admit certain extensions and generalizations of some of the primary assumptions from which we are accustomed to start in theoretical physics, and which hitherto have proved their worth in every field. This becomes necessary in order to find a way out of the difficulty of our dilemma; and it is a result which is sufficiently unsatisfactory to our desire for knowledge. Some consolation can be derived if we see that there is at any rate a possibility of solving the difficulty; consequently I cannot resist the temptation to devote a few words to discussing in what direction it might be possible to find a solution.

The most radical method of avoiding every difficulty would, no doubt, consist in giving up the customary view which holds that radiant energy is localized in some manner or other; i.e. that at every part of a given electromagnetic field, a given amount of energy exists at a given time. If once this assumption is surrendered, the problem ceases to exist, simply because the question whether a light quantum passes through one or the other hole in the opaque screen ceases to have any definite physical meaning. In my opinion, however, this desperate escape from the dilemma goes somewhat too far. For radiant energy as a totality possesses a definite calculable amount; further, the electromagnetic vector-field which is formed by a ray is described in all its optical details, and in the whole of its temporo-spatial behaviour, by classical electrodynamics, and this description agrees exactly with the facts; finally the energy arises and disappears simultaneously with the field. Consequently it is not easy to avoid the question how the distribution of the energy is affected by the details of the field.

Let us decide to pursue this question as far as possible. Then in order to avoid the alternatives with which we are faced, it might appear expedient to retain the fixed connection between the ray, or rather between the electromagnetic wave on the one hand, and the energy attaching to it on the other, but, while retaining it, to give it a wider and less simple meaning than it has in the classical theory. The latter assumes that every part, however small, of an electromagnetic wave contains a corresponding amount of energy proportional to its magnitude, which is supposed to spread concomitantly with the wave. Now if for this fixed connection we substitute something less rigid, it might then appear that the wave emitted from the source of light divides into any number of parts, in conformity with the classical theory, but that at the same time, in accordance with the Quantum Theory, the energy of the wave is concentrated at certain points. The necessary assumption would be that the energy of the wave is not intimately connected with it in its finest detail. On such an assumption, the phenomena of interference would be explained on the lines that even the weakest wave passes partly through one and partly through the other hole in the opaque screen; while on the other hand the photoelectric effect could be explained on the lines that the wave allows its energy to impinge on the electrons only in integral quanta. Here the difficulty consists in trying to imagine part of a light-wave without the energy appropriate to its magnitude;

but though I admit that this is a considerable difficulty, I do not consider it to be essentially greater than that of imagining part of a body without the matter appropriate to its density. Yet we are compelled to make this latter assumption by the fact that matter loses its simple properties if it is subjected to continuous spatial subdivision, since in this case its mass ceases to remain proportional to the space occupied by it, and resolves itself into a number of distinct molecules having a given magnitude. It might well be that the case is closely analogous for electromagnetic energy and the momentum attaching to it.

Hitherto it has been the practice to look for the elementary laws of electromagnetic processes exclusively in the sphere of the infinitely small. Spatially and temporally all electromagnetic fields were divided into infinitely small parts; and their entire behaviour, so far as it appeared subject to laws, was invariably represented by temporo-spatial differential equations. Now in this respect we must radically change our views. For it has been discovered that these simple laws cease to apply after a certain stage in the process of subdivision has been reached, and that beyond this point the increasingly delicate processes make matters more complicated. The spatio-temporal magnitudes of the action become atomic, and we are compelled to assume the existence of elements or atoms of this action. It is indeed a sufficiently striking fact that not a single one of the laws where the universal quantum of action plays a part is expressed by means of a differential equation with a number of continuous variables, but that they all relate to finite times and finite spaces, and deal with such things as definite periods of oscillation, definite orbits, definite transitions, etc. Hence it appears that in order to allow for these facts we must substitute, at least in part, relations between magnitudes at finite distances from each other for those between magnitudes infinitely close to each other. If this is done finite differences take the place of the differential, discontinuity that of continuity, and arithmetic that of analysis; though the substitution admittedly is not carried out radically. A radical substitution is made impossible if only by the claims of the wave theory.

In this direction promising steps have been taken through the development of so-called Quantum Mechanics. This line of investigation has recently produced excellent results in the hands of the Göttingen school of physicists—of Heisenberg, Born and Jordan. Later developments will show how far we can advance towards a solution of the problem along the avenue opened by Quantum Mechanics. Even the choicest mathematical speculations remain in the air so long as they are unsubstantiated by definite facts of experience; and we must hope and trust that the experimental skill of physicists, which in the past has so often definitely decided questions full of doubt and difficulty, will succeed in resolving the difficulties of the present obscure question. In any case there can be no doubt that the parts of the structure of classical Physics, which have had to be discarded as valueless under the pressure of the Quantum Theory, will be supplanted by a sounder and more adequate structure.

To conclude: we have seen that the study of Physics, which a generation ago was one of the oldest and most mature of natural sciences, has to-day entered upon a period of storm and stress which promises to be the most interesting of all. There can be little doubt that in passing through this period we shall be led, not only to the discovery of new natural phenomena, but also to new insight into the secrets of the theory of knowledge. It may be that in the latter field many surprises await us, and that certain views, eclipsed at the moment, may revive and acquire a new significance. For this reason a careful study of the views and ideas of our great philosophers might prove extremely valuable in this direction.

There have been times when science and philosophy were alien, if not actually antagonistic to each other. These times have passed. Philosophers have realized that they have no right to dictate to scientists their aims and the methods for attaining them; and scientists have learned that the starting-point of their investigations does not lie solely in the perceptions of the senses, and that science cannot exist without some small portion of metaphysics. Modern Physics impresses us particularly with the truth of the old doctrine which teaches that there are realities existing apart from our sense-perceptions, and that there are problems and conflicts where these realities are of greater value for us than the richest treasures of the world of experience.

INDEX

OVERLEAF

*particulars of publications
of similar interest
issued by*

GEORGE ALLEN & UNWIN LTD
LONDON: 40 MUSEUM STREET, W.C.1
LEIPZIG: (F. VOLCKMAR) HOSPITALSTR. 10
CAPE TOWN: 73 ST. GEORGE'S STREET
TORONTO: 91 WELLINGTON STREET, WEST
BOMBAY: 15 GRAHAM ROAD, BALLARD ESTATE
WELLINGTON, N.Z.: 8 KINGS CRESCENT, LOWER HUTT
SYDNEY, N.S.W.: AUSTRALIA HOUSE, WYNYARD SQUARE

The Philosophy of Physics
by MAX PLANCK

Crown 8vo   4s. 6d.

"In four short essays the author of the quantum theory discusses some of the deepest problems of the relations of science to philosophy . . . he writes in the simplest language on matters which are of interest and importance to all, whether scientists or not. . . . Into just over a hundred pages this little volume packs an immense amount of stimulating and refreshing thought on some of life's most pressing perplexities."
—*Aberdeen Press and Journal*

You and the Universe
MODERN PHYSICS FOR EVERYBODY
by PAUL KARLSON

Demy 8vo   *Fully Illustrated*   12s. 6d.

You know Van Loon? Well, here is the same humour and clarity, the same aptness in choosing an illustration, which is a revelation. Karlson takes us into the laboratories of the world. He explains what is conjectured about the bricks and mortar of the world, elements, atoms, molecules, about what electricity is, where light comes from, why we see the rainbow in seven colours. He explains how talking films work, talks about wireless and the photo-electric cell, about the structure and infinity of the cosmos.

Professor Schrödinger, winner of the Nobel Prize in Physics, says: "I was surprised by the fantastic richness of your ideas, the ever-changing costumes by which you effectively and permanently keep monotony . . . at arm's length."

"Here is a new way of writing popular science, a new method for bringing home to the layman the hard facts and harder sayings of modern physics . . . an excellent introduction to physics. . . . *You and the Universe* does not pretend to make physics easy—nobody can do that: but it makes it exciting, and it presents it in an entertaining and original way."—
JULIAN HUXLEY in the *Book Society News*

Translations have appeared in Dutch, Italian, Spanish, Polish

Scientific Progress
Sir Halley Stewart Lecture, 1935
by Sir JAMES JEANS, F.R.S.; Sir WILLIAM BRAGG, F.R.S.; Professor E. V. APPLETON, F.R.S.; Professor E. MELLANBY, F.R.S.; Professor J. B. S. HALDANE, F.R.S.; Professor JULIAN HUXLEY

Large Crown 8vo   *Illustrated*   7s. 6d.

"The book can be recommended as a simply and interestingly written authoritative account of the present position on the most important scientific fronts."—*Listener*

"Will give the general reader a clear idea of recent developments in the various fields of science."—*Scotsman*

Science and the Human Temperament
by ERWIN SCHRÖDINGER

TRANSLATED AND EDITED BY JAMES MURPHY

Demy 8vo   7*s.* 6*d.*

Professor Schrödinger was Max Planck's successor in the Chair of Theoretical Physics at the University of Berlin. His name is known throughout the world as the principal author of the wave theory of the constitution of matter. In 1933 he was awarded the Nobel Prize for Physics.

This is a book intended chiefly for the layman. In the first part of it Schrödinger deals with the influence which the dominant ideas in other branches of life—literature, art, sociology, politics, etc.—have on the trends which modern science follows. He shows, for instance, that the statistical trend is characteristic not merely of physical science but also of industry, commerce, social organization, etc. The second part of the book is made up of special lectures which Professor Schrödinger delivered on certain historical occasions, including his address at Stockholm on the occasion of receiving the Nobel Prize. James Murphy has supplied a biographical introduction.

"Professor Schrödinger shows himself an enlightening companion as well as an exponent of the mathematical mysteries."—*Observer*

"The chief importance of Professor Schrödinger's book is the fact that he adds his voice to the many other authorities who would tell us that a new age is here. We have lived to see anthromorphism finally liquidated, elucidated. But we must not, cannot rest there. . . . These essays will help towards clearing our minds on the foundations of science, and they will also serve to introduce to English lay readers one of the framers of the new cosmology."—GERALD HEARD in the *New Statesman and Nation*

The Frustration of Science

by Sir DANIEL HALL, F.R.S.; Dr. J. D. BERNAL; Professor V. H. MOTTRAM; J. G. CROWTHER; Dr. B. M. WOOLF; Dr. PETER GORER; Dr. ENID CHARLES

Crown 8vo   *Second Impression*   3*s.* 6*d.*

"Essays of disillusion, for the most part descriptive, critical. . . . Penned by seven different scientists of some five different academic generations, whose views vary from the mildly radical to the concretely Leninist, they constitute a protest, documented and emphatic, at that frustration of scientific effort against which the book may be taken as in the nature of a manifesto."—*New Statesman and Nation*

What Science Stands For

by Sir JOHN ORR, F.R.S.; Professor A. V. HILL, Sec. R.S.; Professor J. C. PHILIP, F.R.S.; Sir RICHARD GREGORY, Bt., F.R.S.; Sir DANIEL HALL, F.R.S.; Professor LANCELOT HOGBEN, D.Sc., F.R.S.

Crown 8vo   5*s.*

The last meeting of the British Association was plainly notable for an awakening sense of social responsibility among English men of science. Perhaps the most outstanding addresses given at what was certainly a remarkable meeting were those on "Cultural and Social Values of Science," "Knowledge and Power," "Naturalistic Studies in the Education of the Citizen," "A National Food Policy," "The Chemist in the Service of the Community" by the above speakers.

They have now been revised for publication and are presented in this volume, together with a recent broadcast address by Professor A. V. Hill on "The Humanity of Science." They are the views of some outstanding men of science on the scientific worker as citizen and on his attitude to the problems which threaten our civilization.

The History of Science, Technology, and Philosophy in the 16th and 17th Centuries

by Professor A. WOLF
History of Science Library

Sm. Roy. 8vo   Profusely Illustrated from old prints   25*s.*

"Professor Wolf and his colleagues are . . . to be congratulated on something more than the compilation of an admirable history: their work will help to change and to improve the whole teaching of science in our Universities and Schools. No other book of similar scope exists, and none will be necessary for a very long time. . . . The book is written in an abrupt, lucid style which makes even the most complicated of the museum-pieces of theory or practice comprehensible. The diagrams are numerous and clear, and the plates are well chosen."—*Spectator*

Lord RUTHERFORD, O.M., F.R.S.: "A most interesting and valuable book. The author reviews with judgment and perspective the main achievements of that time."

Sir WILLIAM BRAGG, O.M., F.R.S.: "This is a wonderfully interesting and valuable book, beautifully written, well printed and illustrated. Dr. Wolf has done a fine piece of work."

Sir HENRY LYONS, F.R.S.: "In this treatise the physical, biological, and social fields of science are treated fully and with a wealth of references which makes it especially valuable. It fills a long-felt want."

Professor L. N. G. FILON, F.R.S.: "There was never before offered, in so persuasive a manner, a book containing such a mine of useful, yet delightful information."

All prices are net

LONDON: GEORGE ALLEN & UNWIN LTD

Date Due

JAN 8			
De 8 '42			
DEC 7 70			
MAY 1 4			
FE 1 '53			
FEB 1 9 1956			
APR 2 4 1972			
MAR 2 6 1982			
OCT 1 8 1983			
MAR 1 0 1984			
MAY 2 2 1986			
MAY 1 9 1988			
MAY 1 7 1989			